Contents

01
Site organisation

Contents

Supporting information

G: Checklists and forms

GT 700 Toolbox talks

C
01

Overview

In this chapter we provide practical guidance on factors to be considered when preparing to set out a construction site, and details on the other sections of GE 700 that will support this work. This will include information for security, logistics, safety, signs, access and egress.

Generally, much of construction work is transient and therefore the needs of the site can change from day to day. Many of the accidents that occur are caused by poor planning and design during the initial project planning stage.

1.1 Introduction

This chapter aims to give employers and managers general practical guidance on site set-up, the organisation and layout, how it will be run and the effect on people working on it, those living nearby and visitors.

It covers management preparation information, pre-job briefing, competence, site discipline, welfare requirements, security, materials storage, safety signs and utilities.

This chapter also gives an initial introduction to some of the topics found in other sections of GE 700. Its content should be read as well as, not instead of, those sections.

The construction phase plan must record health and safety arrangements for the construction phase, site rules and measures to control particular risks (such as work on high voltage, risk of drowning and underground work).

On site drawings draw or use scale cut-outs of site accommodation, plant and their turning circles, material storage, buildings and temporary works (such as scaffold) and excavation working space to plan site set-up and logistics. Remember to take into account the finished building or structure when decommissioning the site.

One project used a sheet of clear Perspex over a site plan that outlined items such as site accommodation, fencing and temporary roads. Work (such as excavations, crane positions and material storage) were colour coded and plotted daily, which helped identify and plan for potential logistical and safety issues.

1.2 Considerations when setting out a construction site

1.2.1 Existing site features

- Consider previous uses of the site, including contaminated ground or unexploded ordnance that may need to be cleared, and previous storage of dangerous goods or hazardous substances in buildings, cellars or tanks, which might result in substantial site transport movements and additional time and cost.
- Do watercourses need to be protected from contamination?
- Think about isolating underground services or the use of equipment to create barriers or goalposts for live overhead cables. Consider crossing or going around the site if any of these are present.
- Consider the suitability of any existing buildings for intended use. Involve a structural engineer in these processes.
- Check if there is, or could be, any asbestos on the site (refer to existing survey information). Consider whether a refurbishment and demolition survey is needed.
- Identify any protected wildlife or plants.
- Check if any invasive species (such as Japanese knotweed) are present.
- Check if any existing health and safety files or historic records are available of, for example, asbestos in existing buildings/structures on site.
- Consider whether demolition is required as part of this project.

For further information refer to Chapter D08 Underground and overhead services, and Chapter B09 Asbestos.

1.2.2 Site security

A principal contractor must take the necessary steps to prevent access by unauthorised persons. The contractor must not start work unless these steps have been taken, either by themselves (on a one contractor contract) or by the principal contractor (on a project involving more than one person).

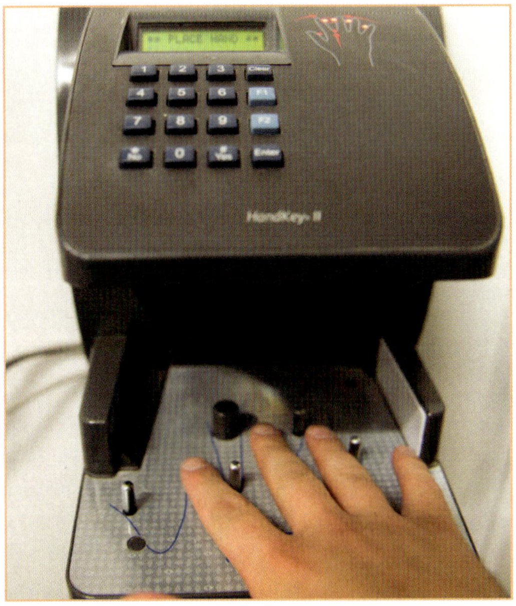

Palm reader controlling access to site

- The perimeter of a construction site must be identified by suitable signs, so it can be recognised, and it must be fenced off.
- Secure the boundary immediately on possession, preferably with lockable gates and suitable hoarding to prevent unauthorised access or fly-tipping.
- If the whole site cannot be secured then ensure areas with potentially hazardous operations are appropriately secured.
- Make specific security arrangements for particular pieces of plant or equipment, if required.
- On larger sites access to the site may be controlled by a biometric system, which can provide a solution for ensuring construction site security.
- Any hoarding or barriers provided to uphold site security and control unrestricted access must be checked to ensure they remain safe throughout the duration of the project.

Baby injured by falling barrier

A construction firm was fined for safety failings after a barrier was blown on top of a pram, injuring an 18-week-old baby.

The construction firm was refurbishing a supermarket and had assembled barriers to separate the public from the work. Branding banners, informing people that the supermarket was still open for business, were attached to the barriers.

The court heard how the baby's mother parked her pram near to the barriers. While her 13-year-old daughter stood next to the pram, the mother walked to the cash machine. She heard her daughter scream and turned to see that the barrier, with the banner attached, had fallen on top of the pram hood, which had then collapsed on the baby. They tried to lift the barrier off the pram, assisted by a passer-by. The baby was taken to hospital with bruising to his forehead. He was discharged later that day and suffered no further effects from the incident.

An investigation by the HSE found that, contrary to the manufacturer's instructions, the barriers had not been filled with water to ensure stability and the barriers next to the cash machines had not been locked together. Inspectors also discovered that high winds had caused the barriers to fall over during the previous month and the site manager had ordered the removal of the banners. Concrete blocks were then placed at the base of the barriers but they were not filled with water.

The construction firm was fined £4,000 after pleading guilty to breaching Section 3 of the Health and Safety at Work etc. Act 1974.

The HSE principal inspector said: 'This incident could easily have been prevented. If assembled correctly the barriers could withstand winds of up to 58 mph. On the day of the incident wind speed was about 30 mph and should not have been an issue'. *(Source: HSE.)*

1.2.3 Temporary works

A competent person must ensure the following.

- They must carry out a foundation assessment and check whether the area for the site cabins is suitable.
- Assess temporary roads for their capability to withstand loads during construction works on the site, especially if they cross existing services.
- Undertake checks for ground bearing capabilities for hard standing for craneage and outriggers.
- Design the site hoardings and gates to withstand wind loadings, particularly to ensure swing gates are managed during high wind conditions. The temporary works forums provide additional information about other conditions for site hoardings.
- Be careful that material storage areas are planned with an awareness of shallow services that can be damaged.
- If a 110 volt distribution system is required check if a live 230/415 volt system is available to power it. Check who will design and install it, and finally who will test and ensure it meets ECA/NICEIC standards.

For further information refer to Chapter C04 Temporary works.

C
01

1.2.4 Pedestrian and traffic routes

- ☑ Provide separate routes for pedestrians and vehicles, with separate entrances if possible.
- ☑ Ensure these entrances minimise traffic hazards on public roads.
- ☑ Any traffic route must not be so uneven, potholed, sloped or slippery that any person is exposed to a risk to their health or safety.
- ☑ Provide a car park for privately owned vehicles, preferably accessed directly from a public road, with entry to the construction area prevented, if practicable.
- ☑ Parking areas should be clearly signposted, firm, level, well lit and not slippery.
- ☑ Ensure that site offices and other facilities are connected to this entrance (for example, for visitors).

The safe separation of construction plant and pedestrians avoids accidents

- ☑ Organise traffic routes to minimise the risk to pedestrians – physical segregation should be used.
- ☑ Ensure safe, designated pedestrian routes are available to all work locations as work progresses.
- ☑ Make use of a turning area if space is tight but try to avoid reversing on site – one way systems are ideal.
- ☑ Ensure availability of competent banksman if reversing is required, if entry onto a site is awkward or pedestrians cannot be completely segregated.
- ☑ Consider the possible requirement for a wheel wash and/or a road sweeper to keep site and public roads clear of mud and other debris.
- ☑ Roads should be wide enough for the vehicles using them.
- ☑ Sharp and blind bends should be avoided. Additional control measures (such as mirrors, stop signs or signals) could be used to help drivers and pedestrians see what is around the corner.
- ☑ A plan of the construction site could be provided at the entrance, which details the traffic management plan and information given to workers.

1.2.5 Internal access routes and housekeeping

Good housekeeping – cables routed along ceiling and over doors to minimise slips and trips

Remind workers to hold the handrail when using the stairs

- Internal access routes need to be kept clear to maintain good housekeeping and reduce fire risks.
- Access routes should be on an even surface, signposted and have adequate lighting.
- Careful consideration should be given to location and routing of temporary electrical supplies.
- If a muddy area on site becomes slippery it should be treated with hardcore.
- If the site is icy it should be treated with grit, or a temporary covering could be provided.
- All obstructions should be kept out of access routes. This can be achieved by providing designated areas for deliveries and waste.

1.2.6 Materials storage and lay-down areas

- Create and communicate a materials delivery schedule.
- Ensure all contractors and suppliers are aware of any delivery restrictions specific to the site or surrounding area (such as schools, low bridges or one way systems).

Marking access routes and providing designated storage areas helps keep walkways tidy and free from obstruction

- Make provision for safe storage to ensure site and access roads are kept clear of obstructions.
- Consider what access is needed to these materials and what lifting equipment may be required (such as telehandlers, forklift trucks, mobile or tower cranes).
- Try to place heavy items (such as heavy goods that need to be moved by hand) near where they will be needed, to avoid double handling.
- Ensure stored materials are stacked appropriately, to avoid them falling and breaching the site boundary.
- Make sure pallets of materials are stored in stable stacks with a safe limit on the height of each.
- Make safe provision for the storage of flammable substances (such as bottled gases and fuels).

For further information refer to:

- **Chapter C07 Lifting operations**
- **Chapter C08 Lifting equipment**
- **Chapter B07 Control of substances hazardous to health.**

1.2.7 Utility services

- Give early consideration to the provision of a 230 volt (mains) supply or a 415 volt three-phase supply when there may be heavy electrical loads (for example, a tower crane).
- Similarly, give early consideration for any provision of telephone and broadband connections.
- Ensure there is a supply of clean water, which must be suitable for drinking, and may require installation by the local water company.
- Make arrangements for the drainage of surface and foul water. The Local Authority needs to be aware of any new connections, and discharge consents are required if waste will be discharged into rivers or other watercourses.
- Gas or oil may be required for heating.
- The size of the site will determine what communication links are needed, including in emergencies.
- Ensure the provision of a generator and appropriate amounts of fuel, where required.

For further information refer to Chapter E01 Sustainable construction and the environment.

1.2.8 Work at height

Various working at height activities

- A risk assessment will determine the most appropriate type of equipment required.
- Consider methods of fall prevention from unloading, including early deliveries for accommodation works (such as fencing and site accommodation).
- Temporary site accommodation, welfare units and containers can be pre-slung or slung using a method that attaches to the bottom of the unit's legs rather than having to access the roof to attach slings to the top of it.
- If scaffolding is being used, it must be erected, altered or dismantled by, or under the direct supervision of, a competent person and be inspected periodically by a competent person.
- If mobile elevating work platforms (MEWPs) are used they must be suitable, operated by competent persons and have adequate ground conditions.

For further information refer to Chapter D01 Work at Height Regulations.

1.2.9 Excavations

- Sufficient working space for spoil, earth work support laydown areas, pipes, plant and machinery must be taken into consideration when planning the work.
- Suitable equipment (such as guard-rails) will be required to form effective, physical barriers around excavations to prevent falls of persons, machinery or vehicles.
- Provide suitably anchored stop blocks or similar devices for the prevention of vehicles, especially tipping dumpers, from falling into excavations.
- If the sides of an excavation need to be supported to prevent falls of soil, rock or materials, then a system of support must be designed by a competent person.
- Ensure safe means of access and egress for persons who need to enter the excavation; this should be by a secured ladder, but avoid the use of service lines.
- Arrangements must be in place for statutory inspections of all excavations.

For further information refer to Chapter D07 Excavations.

1.2.10 Site office

- If the site office has more than one level, particularly where non-construction staff are employed, then temporary planning permission may be required. Also check for any planning restrictions in the contract documents.
- Administrative staff and others, who may not have personal protective equipment (PPE), should have safe access from the car park to the site office.
- Site offices should offer comfortable accommodation for all types of weather and ranges of temperature.
- A suitable, safe form of heating should be provided.
- Provide a suitable electrical supply and telecommunications.
- Compile registers for portable appliance testing, fire alarms and other emergency planning and ensure the site visitors' log is available.
- Consider using temporary accommodation, which often has better environmental performance features than traditional accommodation (such as improved insulation, double glazing, door closers and PIR lighting).

1.2.11 Welfare facilities

- Provide clean and hygienic portable buildings, where workers can change and secure clothing, make a hot drink, heat and eat meals and take shelter in bad weather.
- It may be necessary to provide alternative arrangements until the welfare facilities, power or water connections are made. A variety of standalone, self-contained units are available to suit site needs.
- Additional welfare facilities may be needed for peak workforce levels and provisions should be made for their delivery and installation.
- Where there are both women and men on site, suitable provision must be made for toilet, washing (if necessary, shower) facilities, changing rooms and rest facilities.

Facility for heating food and access to running hot water

Separate male and female site toilets

For further information refer to Chapter B02 Welfare facilities.

1.2.12 First aid

- The appropriate number of qualified first aiders, emergency first aiders or appointed persons will be needed, depending on the number of people and the findings of the first aid needs assessment.
- Details of the first aider(s) and the location(s) of first-aid box(es) must be displayed and communicated. (This could be covered as a topic during site induction.)

For further information refer to Chapter B05 First aid.

1.2.13 Fire safety

- Think about the level of risk from works to be carried out and flammable substances that may be stored and used.
- Any third-party fire arrangements (for example, working in shared or occupied premises) must be maintained and close liaison is vital.
- Provide a sufficient number of fire extinguishers, suitable for the types of fire that might occur, and place them in highly visible fire points in appropriate places, including offices and welfare accommodation.
- Be aware that these points need to be reviewed on a regular basis, given the changing nature of construction sites.
- A suitable number of staff should be trained in the use of the fire extinguishers.
- Fire exit and emergency escape route signs must be displayed, and illuminated in the dark.

For further information refer to Chapter C02 Fire prevention and control.

1.2.14 Emergency plans

- From the start of any project, plans must be put in place for the safe evacuation of the site.
- On complex or refurbishment projects, it is useful to liaise with local fire authorities to identify fire-fighting strategies for the plan, together with the locations of fire-fighting cores, dry risers and lifts or hoists to be used or not used.
- Emergency escape routes must be identified and labelled with appropriate signs and communicated to all on site.
- For larger sites, the emergency plan may be part of the health and safety construction plan and fire wardens may be appointed for specific areas of the site.

- A suitable assembly point should be identified. This should accommodate the maximum number of people, be a safe distance from potential hazards and not be an obstruction or hazard to the emergency services.
- A head count of people on site and who is accounted for must be available in the case of an incident.
- Display information about actions to be taken in an emergency, including what the alarm sounds like, days/times when it will be tested and where the assembly point(s) are.
- Ensure that suitable equipment is provided for use in the event of an environmental emergency (such as spill kits for use with a fuel spillage).
- It is important that workers are trained in the use of spill kits or other equipment provided.

1.2.15 Personal protective equipment

- Employees (including agency workers if they are legally regarded as employees) have a legal duty to be supplied with the necessary PPE free of charge.
- A stock of PPE will need to be held in the site office, to cover specific tasks that may be undertaken by employees or to replace previously issued PPE and for visitors.
- For specific work you may need to seek advice when purchasing respiratory protective equipment (RPE), eye protection, hearing protection and gloves.
- There should always be means to clean, maintain and store PPE.

For further information refer to Chapter B06 Personal protective equipment.

1.3 Safety signs

All safety signs are colour coded, as required by the Health and Safety (Signs and Signals) Regulations.

There are five types of sign, shown below.

- Prohibition.
- Warning.
- Mandatory.
- Emergency escape and first aid.
- Fire-fighting.

1.3.1 Prohibition signs

These signs are round, with a black pictogram on a white background, with red edging and a diagonal red line. They inform people of things they **must not do**: prohibiting the behaviour likely to increase or cause danger.

No smoking

Smoking and naked flames forbidden

No access for pedestrians

Do not extinguish with water

Not drinkable

No access for unauthorised persons

No access for industrial vehicles

Do not touch

1.3.2 Warning signs

These signs are triangular, with a black pictogram on a yellow background, and with black edging. They warn people of a hazard or danger.

Flammable material or high temperature

Explosive material

Toxic material

Corrosive material

Radioactive material

Overhead load

Industrial vehicles

Danger: electricity

General danger

1.3.3 Mandatory signs

These signs are round, with a white pictogram on a blue background. They inform people of things that they **must do**, therefore prescribing a specific behaviour.

Eye protection must be worn

Safety helmet must be worn

Ear protection must be worn

Respiratory equipment must be worn

Safety boots must be worn

Safety gloves must be worn

Safety overalls must be worn

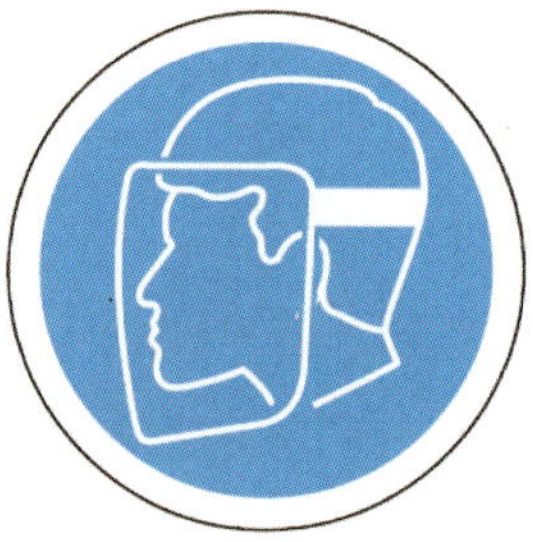

Face protection must be worn

Safety harness must be worn

Pedestrians must use this route

General mandatory sign (to be accompanied where necessary by another sign)

1.3.4 Emergency escape and first aid signs

These signs are rectangular or square, with a white pictogram on a green background. They give information on emergency exits or first-aid facilities.

1.3.4.1 Emergency escape route signs

1.3.4.2 First aid signs

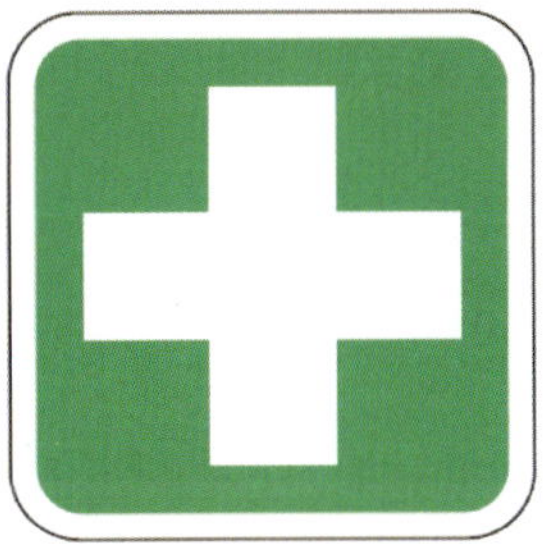

First-aid poster

Stretcher

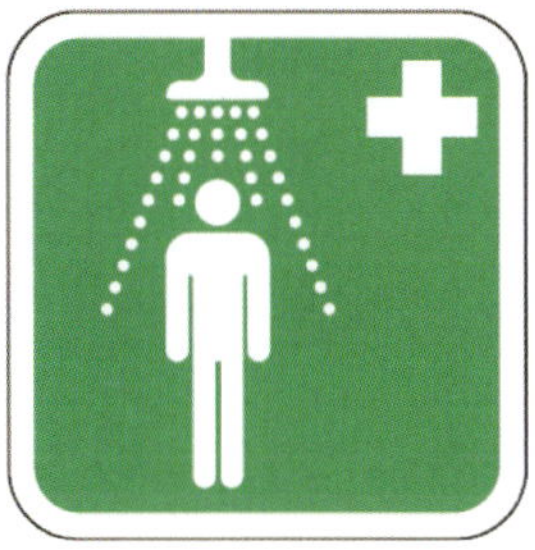

Safety shower

Eyewash

Emergency telephone for first aid or escape

1.3.5 Fire-fighting signs

These signs are rectangular or square, with a white pictogram on a red background. They indicate the location of facilities associated with fire safety.

Fire hose

Ladder

Fire point

Emergency fire telephone

Fire extinguisher telephone

Call point

1.3.6 Signs and notices

Signs for workers to use, to highlight hazards as their working environments change

- ☑ Signs should be displayed at site entrance(s) to inform all persons entering the site about the health and safety requirements for the site. These should include, for example, minimum standards of PPE and state that all visitors must report to the site office.
- ☑ Other signs to be displayed include a selection of appropriate mandatory, warning, prohibition and safe condition signs.
- ☑ Traffic management signs will also be required, as appropriate to the specific site. These may also include directional signage to site and instructions for deliveries.
- ☑ Ensure adequate fire signage (such as showing escape routes, fire assembly points and where the fire points (alarms and extinguishers) are located).
- ☑ Signs will also be required to identify the presence of liquid petroleum gases (LPG) and other flammable substances (such as vehicle and small plant fuels (petrol)).
- ☑ Some types of signs may be used together with other types of communication, for example:
  - illuminated signs and acoustic signals
  - illuminated signs and verbal communication
  - hand signals and verbal communication.

1.4 Environmental considerations

Construction work can impose a severe impact on the environment. Therefore, measures must be taken to prevent or reduce the potential damage.

- ☑ Consider electing an 'environmental champion' for the site.
- ☑ Clearly identify and explain environmental issues in inductions and briefings.
- ☑ Identify and protect watercourses and drainage systems.
- ☑ Ensure you have licences for discharges of proposed water or effluent discharge and arrange for settlement tanks, if appropriate.
- ☑ Have a plan detailing measures to be taken in the event of a spillage (such as preventing seepage into the ground or contaminating watercourses, including sources of drinking water).

- Ensure correct handling, storage and disposal of construction and other types of waste.
- Identify and deal with the existence of protected species of mammals, insects and plants.
- Show how you propose to reduce noise levels, as far as reasonably practicable. You may need to consider restricting some construction processes to certain times.
- Demonstrate a caring attitude towards local residents with regard to site lighting and camera use during night hours.
- By means of risk assessments, reduce the volume of substances used that give off environmentally damaging vapours or fumes.
- Be aware of not causing nuisance to neighbouring properties and do not leave engines running when not in use.

For further information refer to Section E: *Environment*.

1.5 Waste storage and disposal

Waste that is created on a site must be disposed of appropriately. Hazardous waste will need to be stored in appropriate containers and removed by licensed contractors using waste transfer notes.

Non-hazardous waste generated during works undertaken by mobile groups of workers or lone workers can be transported to their base for sorting and transferring to suitable recycling facilities or landfill sites.

A plan to reduce and manage waste should be created before the project begins. Relevant content should also be communicated to contractors and those carrying out the work.

A chute and tipping skip provides the workforce with a quick, safe and easy method to remove waste from a scaffold

The following will need to be considered.

- If the waste is suitable for transporting (hazardous or non-hazardous) and if it requires special handling.
- If the person planning to remove it is competent to do so.
- Provide skips or space for the waste to be segregated (such as plasterboard, metal, timber and electrical waste).
- If asbestos waste is generated, specialist contractors will need to remove it and then transport it to a licensed facility.
- All sites producing hazardous waste must be licensed by the Environment Agency (England), Environment Agency (Northern Ireland), Natural Resources Wales (Wales) or SEPA (Scotland), disposed of by a licensed contractor and be supported by a consignment note.

For further information refer to Chapter E03 Waste management.

1.6 Human factors

1.6.1 Skills, knowledge, training and experience

- To work safely, everyone on site needs to be competent or be supervised closely by someone who is.
- Anyone responsible for putting people to work must ensure they have or are in the process of obtaining the necessary skills, knowledge, training and experience to carry out the job or task in hand.
- You will need to check the competence of contractors/persons coming onto site (such as those persons erecting, altering or dismantling scaffolds, operating site plant, digging excavations and installing the supports or installing traffic management systems).
- One of the earlier competences to check on site would be that of the cabin installer.

1.6.2 Consultation

- Employers must consult and engage with employees or their representatives in good time on issues of health and safety that may affect their health, safety and welfare.
- Employees must be able to raise issues with their employer, directly or through their representatives.
- Where a trade union is recognised, consultation should be through union health and safety representatives. In non-unionised workplaces, consultation should be either direct with workers or through other elected representatives.
- As part of site set-up, consideration must be given as to how effective employer/employee consultation can be achieved.

1.6.3 Co-operation

- The CDM Regulations require all involved in a construction project to co-operate with each other in the interests of health and safety.
- How to achieve this co-operation is best decided at an early stage when the site is being set up.

Whoever you are or whoever you work for, while on a construction site you have a responsibility to ensure you work safely and don't endanger yourself or others by your actions or omissions.

1.7 Contact with emergency services

- You should ensure the local emergency services are informed about the site's location, particularly if it is difficult to locate.
- It is good practice to display, in the site cabin, a road map showing the quickest route to the nearest hospital.
- If you are running a large site, you should nominate an emergency controller to liaise with the emergency services and oversee site emergency actions.

02
Fire prevention and control

Contents

Supporting information

G: Checklists and forms

GT 700 Toolbox talks

C
02

Overview

This chapter outlines the sources of risk that could lead to a fire on site, the measures that should be taken to prevent a fire and additional measures that are necessary to ensure that everyone on site can escape to a safe place and be accounted for, if a fire occurs.

Several major fires have occurred during maintenance work and the refurbishment of premises, simply because hot work was not adequately controlled.

Implementing and maintaining basic measures can eliminate the risk of fires or reduce the risk to an acceptable level.

2.1 Introduction

Fire is an ever-present threat throughout the majority of construction and demolition projects. As construction or demolition progresses the nature of the fire risk is likely to change as different work starts and is completed. Therefore, not only must the risk of fire be managed continuously, but the management process must allow for the changing nature of the risk.

Fires not only put workers' lives at risk but can also result in damage commercially, to reputation and invariably lead to lengthy delays in completion time.

Employers, through their site management structure, must be satisfied that the risk of fire is proactively managed, which includes managing:

- ☑ the everyday fire precautions that are a feature of all sites
- ☑ any additional fire risks that arise out of work processes (for example, hot work)
- ☑ and maintaining fire detection, fire-fighting and fire exit routes.

It is essential that everyone on site knows what to do if the fire alarm sounds, whether it is for real, a practice drill or a false alarm.

Health and safety law places a legal duty on employers to make sure that anyone given a specific role with regard to fire safety is adequately instructed and competent to carry out their responsibilities.

It is in everyone's interest to make sure that, at any point during the construction or demolition process, the risk of fire is understood and adequate protective measures are in place.

2.2 Important points

- ☑ Assess the risk of fire occurring, based upon the chance of a flammable substance and a source of ignition coming together.
- ☑ Take into account any third party fire plans when working in or next to shared premises, especially during refurbishment, repair or maintenance.
- ☑ Put preventative measures in place to ensure fire does not happen.
- ☑ Develop a fire action plan to address any shortcomings, as identified by the fire risk assessment, making sure that higher risks are addressed first.
- ☑ Review and update the fire risk assessment and fire action plan, as necessary, as circumstances change on site.
- ☑ Where circumstances on site demand it, a fire risk manager should be appointed from within the management team to monitor site fire safety and review and update the risk assessment and fire action plan as necessary.
- ☑ Communicate the significant findings of the fire risk assessment, and any significant changes to it, to everyone on site.
- ☑ Inform the fire and rescue service (FRS) of the location of bulk stores of flammable materials, particularly liquefied petroleum gas (LPG) and other explosive gases.
- ☑ Put in place a hot-work permit scheme to control the way in which high risk activities are carried out.
- ☑ Pay particular attention to the manner in which bulk flammable materials (such as timber, gases, adhesives and highly flammable liquids) are stored.
- ☑ Make sure that fire safety is included as a part of site induction, including what site staff should do in the event of a fire.

- As far as emergency escape measures are concerned:
  - appoint at least one person to call the emergency services
  - make sure that there are always sufficient emergency escape routes to allow safe evacuation, from all parts of the site, by the maximum number of people likely to use each route
  - regularly check that escape routes are kept clear and are not blocked by changes to work (such as erecting a mobile tower on a staircase or in a corridor that is an escape route)
  - identify emergency escape routes by installing fire exit signs that direct people to a place of safety via the shortest safe route, and move the signs if necessary should the emergency escape routes have to be altered
  - ensure there is a suitable fire alarm system that can be heard in all parts of the site
  - identify, with signs, assembly point(s) to where site staff should report after a site evacuation.
- Provide an adequate number of clearly identified fire points that are equipped with appropriate types of fire extinguisher.
- Train sufficient people in the selection and use of fire extinguishers to enable small fires to be dealt with before they can become larger, more serious fires.
- Pay particular attention to fire safety in site accommodation:
  - a complex of interlinked or multistorey, site cabins is likely to make it necessary to appoint one or more fire wardens to assist in an emergency evacuation
  - such accommodation can quickly become smoke-logged in a fire, increasing the risk of smoke inhalation and possibly creating disorientation and panic in anyone trying to escape
  - it could be argued that the extensive use of mains-powered office equipment and electric heating increases the fire risk.
- If cylinders containing LPG, or any other explosive gas, are being heated in a fire:
  - the emergency services must be called immediately
  - there is a risk of a major explosion with the cylinders becoming airborne projectiles
  - attempts to fight the fire must not be made by site staff
  - a prompt site evacuation must be carried out and everyone accounted for
  - upon their arrival the FRS will need to know the location of the cylinders and will organise a 200 m cordon around the site.

Fire safety can be a complex issue on large, fast-moving sites with significant numbers of people to evacuate. Where the expertise is not present on site or within the company, it is advisable to seek the advice of a fire safety specialist.

In this chapter, in most cases, where the word 'construction' appears the point being made will also be applicable to demolition. However, for simplicity's sake only the word 'construction' will be used.

2.3 Legislative requirements

The Regulatory Reform (Fire Safety) Order (FSO) applies to premises, including workplaces. Therefore, a construction site in England and Wales could be deemed to be a workplace. Areas of the construction site include occupied extensions that remain part of the construction site and under site management control, office accommodation, and so on. In Scotland requirements on general fire safety are covered in Part 3 of the Fire (Scotland) Act, supported by the Fire Safety (Scotland) Regulations. The Fire Safety Regulations (Northern Ireland) apply in Northern Ireland.

A responsible person, under the order, is anyone who has control of premises or anyone who has a degree of control over certain areas of systems (for example, a responsible person could be the project manager or the employer.) On sites where there are a number of people with responsibilities, this person should be named.

The FSO requires that a responsible person must carry out a risk assessment and then keep this up to date. Appropriate control measures must be implemented to minimise the risk, to life and property, from fire.

The responsible person must make sure that everyone on the premises can escape safely if there is a fire. In Scotland the responsible person is known as the *competent person*. For further information refer to Scottish fire legislation.

The Construction (Design and Management) Regulations (CDM) outline the responsibilities with regard to the prevention of fires on sites and emergency procedures, routes and exits, fire detection and fire fighting.

If something goes wrong with regard to fire safety and an external investigation takes place, one or more of the enforcement agencies will visit the site to conduct an investigation and interviews.

The enforcement of fire safety legislation on construction sites is complex and is dependent upon the nature of the site and what work is being carried out.

Responsibility for the enforcement of fire safety legislation is split between the following.

- The HSE, or possibly the Local Authority on small sites, either of which would usually take enforcement action under the CDM Regulations or the Management of Health and Safety at Work Regulations. However, the HSE also has enforcement powers under the Regulatory Reform (Fire Safety) Order (England and Wales). This is in relation to any premises for which a licence is required, in accordance with Section 1 of the Nuclear Installations Act or, for which a permit is required, in accordance with Section 2 of that Act. It also applies to any premises which would, except for the fact that it is used by, or on behalf of, the Crown, be required to have a licence or permit.
- The local FRS, which would enforce their powers under the Regulatory Reform (Fire Safety) Order (England and Wales) or the Fire (Scotland) Act (Scotland only).

For enforcement purposes, construction sites are divided into three categories.

1. Completely **segregated and separate** construction sites, with their own perimeter fence or hoarding, upon which the only activity carried out is construction work.

   In this case, both general fire precautions (GFP) and process fire safety issues are enforced by the HSE, although the FRS will be the enforcing body over any temporary accommodation units that are outside the site boundary.
2. Construction sites in shared or occupied premises that have an **unbreached and continuous** fire-resistant wall to separate the construction work from the occupier's work.

   In this situation, a fire in the construction part of the premises would not affect the other occupied area(s) and consequently both GFP and process fire safety issues are again enforced by the HSE within the construction site area, with the FRS enforcing them in the other occupied parts of the building.
3. Construction sites in occupied or shared premises where there is a **breached** (not totally fire or smoke-proof) partition or wall between the construction and the occupier's work, so that a fire in either section would have implications for the other section.

   In this situation, the HSE is the enforcing body with respect to the GFP in the construction area, whilst the FRS is the enforcing body with respect to process fire safety.

The FRS will also be the enforcing authority for off-site premises (such as a company's head office premises or a storage yard).

2.4 Nature of fire

2.4.1 Conditions for a fire to start

In order to take the measures required to prevent fires starting, it is first necessary to understand the conditions that must be present to enable a fire to start.

Three factors are necessary for fires to burn.

- **Fuel** or combustible material. Any material or substance, whether liquid, solid or gas, which will burn given sufficient amounts of heat and a supporter of combustion, such as air or oxygen.
- **Heat** or ignition source. Every fuel has an ignition temperature. All solids and liquids give off vapour when heated, and it is this vapour that ignites.
- **Air** (or other supporter of combustion, such as oxygen) which is always there to sustain fire, providing the other factors are present.

Once a fire has started, if any one of these factors is isolated or removed, the fire will be extinguished.
This can be achieved by:

- removing the fuel or combustible material, leaving nothing to burn
- removing the heat by applying water to cool the burning material
- reducing or excluding the air or oxygen by smothering the burning material. Foam, dry powder, carbon dioxide (CO_2) and fire blankets are all smothering agents.

2.4.2 How fire can be spread

Fire can be spread in four ways:

- conduction
- convection
- radiation
- direct burning.

Conduction is where heat is transmitted from one place to another along or through solid material (such as along a metal pipe or through a door or wall). The conduction of heat therefore has the potential to start a fire in a location that is remote from the original source of heat.

Convection occurs where superheated gases or heat rising from a fire ignites other combustible material or when particles of burning material in the circulating air are deposited in another place, causing another fire.

Radiation is the transfer of radiated heat from the fire, through the air directly to other flammable materials nearby, which will cause those materials to be raised to their ignition temperature and then burn.

Direct burning is a combination of conduction, convection and radiation and is where the fire spreads and reaches other combustible materials and ignites them, adding further fuel to the fire.

2.5 Principles of fire risk management

The Health and Safety Executive (HSE) regards major construction site fires as low frequency and high impact events. The effects of a major fire can be devastating for those working on the site and also those living and working nearby. Fires on large, timber-frame projects have resulted in multiple secondary fires, spread over a large area, and the destruction of adjacent businesses and domestic accommodation. The resulting damage and investigations stop all work on the site for a significant length of time with consequences for the people who work there and the employer(s) who may face enforcement action by the HSE or the FRS, potentially putting the future viability of those companies in doubt.

As soon as any item of plant or a site cabin arrives on site, the risk of fire occurring is increased and the situation must be managed. As the job progresses, various work will start and be completed and the level of fire risk will vary. It is the dynamic nature of construction sites that makes continual attention to fire risk management so important.

On many projects, as the structure is gradually completed, areas within it become enclosed by rooms, corridors, plant rooms, and so on. At that time, any fire is likely to cause smoke-logging within the areas affected, when toxic smoke will progressively fill the area, displacing breathable oxygen.

It is perhaps at this time that a fire would be most dangerous to those working on site.

- ☑ There are likely to be more flammable materials incorporated within the fabric of the structure.
- ☑ The smoke is a toxic hazard.
- ☑ Escape routes are likely to be longer as the internal walls and partitions are built.
- ☑ By its dense, black nature, the smoke could make it more difficult to determine the exact path of the escape route (for example, from a multi-room basement, through smoke-logged corridors and up to street level).
- ☑ In an emergency situation, people can panic and may not act in a rational manner.

Whilst any fire on site will create a potentially dangerous situation, it is considered that, in many cases, the threat to personal safety during a fire greatly increases as the structure is nearing completion. By the very nature of the operations carried out (cutting, burning, grinding, welding, and so on), the use of flammable substances and the amount of wood and other combustible materials used or stored on site, the potential for fire is always present and must be effectively managed.

- ☑ Take steps to prevent a fire from starting in the first place (managing the process fire risks).
- ☑ Prepare for, effectively react to, and limit the effects of a fire if it does occur (managing the general fire precautions).

Fire safety law requires that in every workplace a **responsible person** is appointed, whose duty it is to see that the law is complied with, in that effective fire risk management measures are put in place and monitored. In law it would, in most cases, be the employer who would be regarded as the responsible person. However, as with other health and safety legislation, where the employer is not site based, the day-to-day, on-site management of the risks will be delegated to the site manager.

The following text highlights some of the common factors that have to be considered when deciding how best to manage the risk of fire on site.

2.6 Fire risk assessment

If the FRS or enforcing authority visit a site they will expect to see a site-specific fire risk assessment that addresses current and future fire risk issues. This legal requirement derives from the Regulatory Reform (Fire Safety) Order and the CDM Regulations. Generic fire risk assessments and those with irrelevant and unsatisfactory details copied and pasted from previous jobs will not be acceptable. The responsible person is required to carry out and maintain a fire safety risk assessment. This is under the Regulatory Reform (Fire Safety) Order and under Part 3 of the Fire (Scotland) Act.

If you do not properly assess the risks, there is no way that you can adequately control them.

The principles of carrying out a fire risk assessment are broadly the same as for other risk assessments, although the recommended steps are slightly different to those outlined for more general risk assessments in the **Management of Health and Safety at Work Regulations**.

There are five steps when carrying out a fire risk assessment.

1. Identify the fire hazards that will be present on site during the period covered by the risk assessments.
2. Identify the people who will be at risk, which may include people who are not actually on site.
3. Evaluate those risks, plan how to remove or reduce them and how to protect people from any risks that remain.
4. Record the significant findings of the risk assessment, develop an emergency plan and inform and instruct those on site regarding the fire risks identified.
5. Periodically review the fire risk assessment to ensure it is still valid, update it as necessary and communicate the changes to those at risk.

The HSE publication *Fire safety in construction* (HSG168) covers this in more detail.

In many cases, carrying out a fire risk assessment will be relatively straightforward, simple and can be carried out by the responsible person or someone nominated by them to do it. In most cases the responsible person on a site will be the contractor or principal contractor.

On small jobs the initial assessment might be valid all the way through to completion. On larger or complex sites, where perhaps there are a greater number of people to evacuate in an emergency or there are long travel distances to a place of safety, someone with a detailed knowledge of fire risk management (such as a consultant) may be required. In this scenario, it is likely that periodic reviews and updates of the assessment will be required.

Irrespective of the size or complexity of the project, anyone carrying out a fire risk assessment must be competent to do so, in that they can accurately identify the hazards, assess the risks and put effective control measures in place.

A guide to choosing a competent fire risk assessor has been published by the Fire Risk Assessment Competency Council. For this and further documents to help you ensure you are competent to undertake risk assessments, refer to the Fire Industry Association and Institution of Fire Engineers websites.

For a sample fire risk assessment, in the format recommended by the HSE, refer to Section G: _Checklists and forms_.

2.6.1 Stage 1. Identify the fire hazards

Anything that burns is fuel for a fire; in general, fires start in one of three ways.

1. Accidentally (for example, when an inspection of a work area after hot work has been carried out fails to discover smoldering materials).
2. By act or omission (such as in the example above, if the inspection was simply not carried out).
3. Deliberate arson attack on the structure or, for example, a waste skip.

Therefore the assessor should consider how a fire could start and what could burn.

Some examples of the risks that could be considered are shown below.

- The use of any equipment that incorporates a naked flame, hot air stream or hot surface.
- Preventing the use of faulty electrical equipment.
- Making sure that electrical equipment is not misused (for example, by overloading circuits).
- The periodic testing and inspection of electrical circuits and equipment, including safety devices.
- The safe disposal of discarded smoking materials in the areas where smoking is allowed.
- The use of temporary lighting, particularly halogen floodlights.
- Heat generated by operating plant.
- The use of heating and cooking appliances.

Potential fire risks

- Compile an inventory of the flammable materials that are, or will be, present and where they will be stored and used.
  Consider whether anything can be done to reduce the risk by:
  – altering work processes so that hot work is not necessary
  – using alternative, less-flammable materials
  – reducing the number or quantities of flammable materials on site at any one time.
- Make sure they are stored and used away from sources of ignition, unless unavoidably used as part of a hot-work process.
- Identify the sources of ignition that are, or will be, present, taking account of, for example, hot works that are scheduled in the future.

2.6.2 Stage 2. Identify the people at risk

Everyone is at risk if there is a fire. Therefore, the assessor should consider the following.

- ☑ Decide who are the individuals and/or groups of people likely to be at risk if a fire breaks out and if anyone could be at a greater risk (for example, shift workers, visitors who are unfamiliar with the site, and so on).
- ☑ Consider whether anyone is at an enhanced level of risk because of what they do, where they work or because of a disability (such as a lack of mobility or reduced hearing). The Equality Act requires employers not to discriminate against any person because of their disability and to make reasonable adjustments to match the need of the disabled personnel. A personal emergency evacuation plan (PEEP) may be required in these circumstances.
- ☑ Consider the impact that a fire would have on neighbouring properties and all forms of traffic passing the site. For example, the FRS will impose a 200 m cordon and evacuation zone around any fire in which gas cylinders are involved. Such a fire can involve evacuating many people and closing major traffic routes, including railway lines.

2.6.3 Stage 3. Evaluate, remove, reduce and protect from the risk

Having determined the hazards and who is likely to be harmed, the responsible person must take the necessary actions to reduce the risks to an acceptable level.

This is a two-stage process that involves considering the following questions.

1. What are the risks of the fire starting?
2. What are the risks to people on the site and nearby?

There are potentially many practical measures that can be taken to reduce the risk of a fire occurring.

- ☑ Ensuring that electrical office equipment, electrical appliances and portable hand tools are PAT tested at appropriate intervals to identify any defects.
- ☑ The effective quarantine of defective electrical equipment awaiting repair (or disposal if not repairable).
- ☑ Routinely testing electrical distribution systems.
- ☑ Storing flammable and highly flammable liquids in appropriately constructed and sited secure stores that prevent the escape of spillages or impact by traffic or plant.
- ☑ Storing gas cylinders in secure stores that allow any leakage to disperse, with the separation of some gases as is necessary.
- ☑ Prohibiting the refuelling of petrol or diesel-powered equipment and plant whilst it is still hot.
- ☑ The regular inspection and maintenance as necessary of any system that carries a flammable gas or liquid (such as the supply pipework to oxy-fuel sets, cabin heaters, the canteen cooker or a stand-by generator).
- ☑ Not allowing oxy-fuel sets to be used unless flashback arrestors are fitted to the pipework.
- ☑ Preventing arson by putting in place effective security measures, both within and outside of site operating hours.
- ☑ The introduction and effective implementation of a hot-works permit system for high risk activities.
- ☑ Ceasing hot work at least one hour (two hours for higher risk sites, such as large, timber-frame projects) before site closure, and regularly monitoring the work area and surrounding structure in the intervening time.
- ☑ Maintaining a strict smoking policy; if smoking is permitted in certain areas of the site, provide safe means of disposing of used smoking materials.

Similarly, there are many practical measures that can be taken to reduce the risk to people if a fire should occur.

- ☑ Making fire safety and evacuation procedures part of site induction, so site staff know what to do if there is a fire, who will call the emergency services, what escape routes should be used, and so on.
- ☑ Understanding how fires spread and what actions to take in the event of a fire.
- ☑ Maintaining a strict regime of clearing up solid, flammable waste materials and putting them in skips.
- ☑ Ensuring that any flammable liquid waste is stored safely and disposed of at the first opportunity.

2.6.4 Stage 4. Record the findings, prepare an emergency plan and provide training

2.6.4.1 Record

Where there are five or more employees, the significant findings of the risk assessment, including details of any actions taken to reduce the fire risk, must be recorded in a manner that can be easily retrieved should it be necessary to do so. Even when there are fewer than five employees, it is good practice to record the **significant** findings of the fire risk assessment. The risk assessment will also assist in developing the emergency plan and will show more clearly where weaknesses in fire risk management lie. If called upon by the enforcing authority to provide evidence of sound fire risk management practices, a written risk assessment is far preferable to a verbal briefing.

The word **significant** allows the risk assessor to ignore trivial risks of fire. The position of the dividing line between trivial and significant is subjective but it is advisable to err on the side of caution.

Points that require recording include the following.

- Significant fire hazards identified.
- How the hazards will be eliminated.
- Preventative measures that will be taken to reduce the risk of fire from those hazards that cannot be eliminated.
- People who are at risk.
- Actions that have been taken to reduce the spread of fire and smoke if a fire should occur.
- Details of the general fire precautions (such as the maintenance of escape routes, and the location and maintenance of fire-fighting equipment), plus any fire extinguisher training given.
- Details of any instructions given to individuals regarding the actions to take to prevent fires and to escape from the site safely if a fire does occur.
- Details of people with particular fire safety responsibilities (such as the responsible person, fire safety co-ordinator and fire warden).

Record other fire-related issues, including the delivery of appropriate toolbox talks and other fire-related briefings. These records could be useful at a later date.

2.6.4.2 Prepare emergency plan

The findings of the fire risk assessment will help prepare a plan of how the fire can be prevented and how the site staff will be kept safe in the event of a fire. If the site adjoins occupied premises (for example, a hospital or existing business) the plan may need to be co-ordinated with that of theirs.

2.6.4.3 Train

All site staff need to know what action to take in the event of a fire and if necessary understand any specific roles they may be required to carry out.

Workers should know what to do in the event of a fire

Correct training should be given, as required, and should include the following.

- The significant findings of the fire risk assessment.
- The measures that have been put in place to reduce the risk.
- What people should do in the event of a fire, including temporary staff.
- The identity of people with responsibilities for fire safety (such as fire wardens).
- Any special arrangements that are necessary to protect people on site from serious or imminent danger from fire.

It will also be necessary to provide training on the selection and use of portable fire extinguishers to an appropriate number of staff.

2.6.5 Stage 5. Review and update the fire risk assessment regularly

Due to the ever-changing nature of construction sites, the review of the fire risk assessment is very important. A review provides the opportunity to critically examine the effectiveness of the fire risk assessment with regard to site conditions at that time and to update it as necessary. If significant changes in risks are identified or changes are made to the plan site staff and those in adjoining premises must be informed and retained as required.

For example, consider the changes that might be necessary as a result of the following.

- Last week's escape route becoming a dead-end today.
- The increasing complexity of escape routes as large structures are built.
- A significant increase in people on site since the last review.
- The start of a hot-work process.

- The start of a new activity that necessitates the storage of flammable substances (such as LPG and other gases) in bulk.
- The need to extend the fire detection system.
- A poorly carried out practice evacuation.
- The occurrence of a fire-related near miss.

Many local FRS will provide guidance on carrying out fire risk assessments.

2.7 Fire action plan

Through a well thought out action plan, you will be better prepared to prevent fire and to cope with one should it occur.

Depending upon the findings of the fire risk assessment, it will normally be necessary to compile a fire action plan to enable the person responsible for fire safety to keep track of fire risks, on a day-by-day basis, throughout the project and to adjust preventative and protective measures as required.

The fire action plan must be compiled and updated as necessary by a person who is competent to:

- identify the potential fire and explosion risks
- appreciate when these may change, particularly if they significantly increase
- implement the measures necessary to minimise the risk of fire and explosion, and mitigate the effects if a fire does occur.

The person(s) selected to do this may come from within the existing site management team or, where particular expertise is required, from a consultancy or specialist fire safety practice. In many cases it will not be the same person who is the responsible person in law.

Examples of sites where external expertise might be required are shown below.

- Those that are large in area with a high number of people to evacuate via multiple escape routes.
- Where the structure being built or refurbished has several floors with limited access between them.
- Those that have long or complex escape routes with changes in direction and level.

The nature of the fire action plan will depend upon many factors (such as the size of the site and the fire risks arising out of the type of work being carried out). In many cases it will be a formal document that forms a part of the construction phase plan, compiled in accordance with CDM.

On smaller sites and/or where the fire-related hazards are familiar and simpler to manage, a formal fire action plan may not be required. If this is the case or if only a simple fire action plan is required, the contractor, or principal contractor where appointed, will be responsible for this.

The principal contractor or contractor should be responsible for the following.

- Compiling the fire action plan, regularly reviewing it and updating it as necessary.
- Making sure that the content (in whole or part) of the fire action plan is communicated to all who need to know (for example, publicising the evacuation procedure to operatives during site induction sessions).
- If necessary, identifying a fire warden to assist in promoting and updating the plan and in site evacuations (these can be appointed from the other companies on site).
- Ensuring that relevant parts of the site fire safety plan are clearly understood by all on the site and are covered during site induction.
- Ensuring fire action notices are displayed on noticeboards and next to fire alarm call points.
- Implementing a system to locate site visitors, getting them to an allocated assembly point and accounting for them after an evacuation.
- If necessary, establishing a hot-work permit system and monitoring its effectiveness.
- Ensuring that regular checks of the fire-fighting equipment and facilities are carried out.
- Ensuring that the site fire action plan is clearly understood and complied with by all those on the site.
- Ensuring that all alarms and detection devices are tested at least weekly.
- Arranging for the routine testing and inspection of fire-fighting appliances and for items to be serviced or replaced, as necessary.
- Carrying out weekly inspections of emergency escape routes, and more frequent inspections if deemed necessary due to fast-moving or changes in circumstances.
- Ensuring that access for the emergency services is always maintained.
- Liaising with the emergency services as necessary.

- Liaising on matters of fire safety with site security staff.
- Liaising with any third parties that could be affected (for example, neighbouring properties, highways or railways).
- Putting in place the arrangements for calling the emergency services.
- Instigating practice evacuation drills and, in conjunction with the fire warden, monitoring the effectiveness of the procedure in terms of:
  - the time taken to evacuate the site
  - any problems in accounting for everyone on site
  - the need for any improvements to the evacuation procedure that become apparent.
- Monitoring the efficiency of the evacuation procedure during genuine emergency situations and again implementing procedures where necessary.

The fire action plan should include the following details.

- An organisation chart for fire risk management, where necessary.
- The names and positions of persons and their responsibilities for the various aspects of fire safety (for example, calling the emergency services).
- General site fire precautions.
- The location and type of fire-fighting appliances and arrangements for their servicing and inspection.
- The location of the fire assembly point(s), with details of the persons/companies assigned to each, where there is more than one.
- Process fire risks (for example, hot works).
- Details of the fire detection and warning alarms installed on site.
- Arrangements for maintaining fire escape routes in an unobstructed state and changing them, as necessary, as work progresses.
- Arrangements for notifying all on site of the emergency escape routes and any changes to them.
- Procedures for implementing a hot-work permit system, if one is in use.
- Details of all site temporary accommodation units, their uses and particular fire hazards (such as a cooking range).
- The fire evacuation plan.
- The access route(s) for the emergency services and making sure they are kept clear.
- Fire drills and training, and the procedure for maintaining written records.

For an example of a fire risk management action plan refer to Section G: *Checklists and forms*.

2.8 Emergency procedures

The person with responsibility for fire safety must consider the following areas at all stages of the project and then review, revise and communicate the changes of the fire risk assessment and fire action plan to those who are at risk, as necessary.

2.8.1 Fire alarm systems

In the event of a fire, it is essential that the alarm is raised as quickly as possible so that employees and others (such as visitors) can quickly and safely reach a place of safety.

Sites must have an effective fire alarm system

Alarms must be sufficient in number and location so that everyone on site is aware that the alarm has sounded. Hand bells, klaxons or manually, electrically or wireless operated sounders may be suitable so long as they are clearly audible above background noise in all areas and can be readily identified as being a fire alarm. Flashing lights or vibrating pagers may be required in certain circumstances (for example, where there is continuous or frequent loud noise).

With the availability of low-cost wireless technology, the size or complexity of the site would not be regarded as a valid barrier to having effective fire warning and alarm systems.

2.8.2 Fire action notices

Legible, written emergency procedures (fire action notices) must be displayed in prominent locations around the site, and should include the following.

- ☑ The location of the notice to enable the location of the fire to be pinpointed.
- ☑ Instructions for raising the alarm.
- ☑ Instructions for calling the FRS.
- ☑ Instructions to report to the nearest assembly point.
- ☑ Clear information as to the whereabouts of the assembly point.
- ☑ A clear instruction not to leave the assembly point until a roll call has been taken.
- ☑ An indication of the locations of fire escape routes.
- ☑ An instruction not to re-enter the building or site until it has been declared safe to do so by someone in authority.

2.8.3 Emergency escape routes

There must be sufficient escape routes from all parts of the site to a place of safety, in the open air and at ground level. During the construction phase escape routes are likely to change. Therefore, the routes should be reviewed and alternative routes identified and communicated to all staff, as required.

Escape routes will ideally be determined at the design stage to ensure their continued integrity and should be installed as soon as possible during the construction phase. The escape routes must be:

- ☑ adequate with regard to the number of people likely to use them, bearing in mind that this is likely to change on a regular basis on fast-moving sites
- ☑ always available in case of fire
- ☑ kept free of obstructions and checked that they are unobstructed at least weekly
- ☑ altered as necessary as the project advances
- ☑ equipped with adequate signage and lighting (possibly including emergency lighting) as necessary, all of which must be moved as the escape routes change.

Doors leading onto any staircase must be self-closing and have a half-hour fire resistance. If fire doors are required to be locked when the site is unoccupied, due to security reasons, then these must be unlocked as soon as the site is opened. Preferably all security locks should comply with the relevant British safety standards, therefore removing the need for a key lock.

2.8.4 Fire drills

Emergency evacuations should be practised at suitable intervals. These intervals will depend on many factors, including the complexity of the site, additional hazards and evolving nature of the site. They will vary from site to site, and may even vary on the same site as work progresses, but they must not exceed one year.

Practicing emergency evacuations will provide evidence of suitability and the effectiveness of the alarm signal (for example, it may prove that it cannot be heard in some areas). It will also show any bottlenecks where there could be problems in a real emergency unless action is taken. Everyone should be made aware of what the alarm signal sounds like during site induction and the timing of any regular testing for which no action is necessary. Records should be kept of all evacuations.

An accurate system of booking in and out of the site is absolutely essential to enable the person running an evacuation to know who is on site at any time.

No-notice drills provide the most useful information on the effectiveness of the evacuation procedure, but it is recognised that in many cases such drills will be impractical. However, even pre-notified drills will provide information on evacuation time and the problems faced by fire wardens in the event of a fire or emergency.

2.8.5 Emergency lighting

Emergency lighting is required to ensure that escape routes can be seen. In the event of failure of the primary lighting the emergency lighting needs to come on immediately.

Emergency lighting can be powered by batteries or an emergency generator.

2.8.6 Fire detection systems

During the early stages of new-build projects it is inevitable that the only way of detecting fires is visually; someone will spot a fire and raise the alarm. However, on larger and higher risk sites, as areas within a structure become enclosed, with increasing amounts of flammable materials present, the benefits of an automatic fire detection become obvious. Where a permanent automatic fire detection system is planned, activation of the system should be programmed in as early as possible.

During refurbishment work, which has been the cause of many serious fires, if an automatic fire detection system already exists, it should remain live throughout the work where it is practical to do so.

2.8.7 Fire-fighting equipment

An extensive range of equipment is available for fighting fire. *(For further information on fire-fighting equipment refer to 2.14.)*

2.8.8 Smoking restrictions

Smoking in enclosed and substantially enclosed workplaces is now banned in England and Wales, Scotland and Northern Ireland. The following advice refers to situations where smoking is allowed in some non-enclosed areas.

Given that smoking in the open air is not prohibited, site rules must be established to ensure that, where required, safe smoking areas are available. Where these are provided, provision should be made for the safe disposal of spent smoking materials, as carelessly discarded smoking materials have the potential to cause fires on site. The designated area must be away from combustible and flammable materials, and be equipped with adequate fire-fighting equipment.

As work progresses and the site develops it will be necessary to monitor the changes in the fire risk areas and review the areas where smoking is allowed accordingly.

2.8.9 Fire wardens

Clearly identifiable fire marshal/warden

The competent person may, in consultation with the principal or contractor, need to arrange for the appointment of fire wardens to assist in the evacuation of the site, and the implementation of the site fire action plan. A fire warden may also be known as a fire marshal.

On large sites it is usual for at least one fire warden to be appointed from each company of sub-contractors to account for that company's staff in the event of a site evacuation.

Where fire wardens' duties are more extensive, they must be allowed sufficient time to carry out their duties and to undertake any training that may be necessary.

2.8.10 Specialist advice

The Fire Protection Association (FPA), in conjunction with the Construction Confederation (CC), published the eighth edition of *Fire prevention on construction sites* in July 2012. This joint Code of Practice (CoP) deals with the protection from fire on construction sites and buildings undergoing renovation.

The CoP does not have any legal status; however, it does outline good practice and many insurance companies now require that the authoritative guidelines (such as those detailed in the CoP) are properly implemented on construction projects before they will give full insurance.

This chapter broadly outlines the requirements of the CoP.

www.

The FPA also publishes *Construction site fire prevention checklist – a guide for insurers, surveyors and construction industry professionals*.

2.8.11 Liaison with the fire and rescue service (FRS)

Contact should be made with the FRS at an early stage of the project, if it is envisaged that there will at some time be significant quantities of flammable materials (of any type) on site, to enable them to plan their response to any emergency. It is likely that the FRS will visit the site as a result.

A site layout plan should be made available to the FRS, as should any updated versions of it. The site layout plan should indicate the following.

- An FRS access point if there is more than one site access.
- Emergency escape routes.
- The location of fire points and other fire-fighting equipment.
- The location of flammable and highly flammable material storage areas (particularly LPG).
- Positions and types of fire alarm sounders.
- Location of assembly point(s).

The FRS are likely to be particularly interested in sites where:

- there is a significant fire risk to the public resulting from a large scale evacuation of a high number of people
- large or high fire risk structures (such as multistorey timber frame) are to be built close to other occupied premises
- highly flammable materials will be stored and used
- there may be difficult access to the site by the FRS
- work will take place above 18 m, in which case specialist access equipment is required
- work is taking place in a building that is partially occupied by others.

2.8.12 Fire action notices

Legible written emergency procedures must be displayed in prominent locations within offices and should include:

- the location of the notice to enable the location of the fire to be pinpointed (for example, first-floor photocopier room)
- instructions for raising the alarm
- instructions for calling the FRS
- instructions to report to the nearest assembly point
- clear information as to the whereabouts of the assembly point
- a clear instruction not to leave the assembly point until a roll call has been taken
- an indication of the locations of fire escape routes
- an instruction not to re-enter the building or site until it has been declared safe to do so by someone in authority.

2.9 Common sources of fire risk

2.9.1 Storage and use of flammable materials

Many materials and substances used in the construction process will readily catch fire if exposed to a source of ignition. Additionally, other potentially flammable and explosive substances that are not directly used within the construction process (such as vehicle fuels and gases for cooking and heating within site accommodation) also pose a fire risk if not stored and used correctly.

- Where practical, all combustible materials should be stored outside the structure under construction, particularly potentially high risk flammable materials (such as petrol and LPG). Ideally all materials will be stored in a locked compound or storage container, with adequate separation between different types of product. Where internal storage is inevitable, the storage area must:
  - **not** be located so that it poses a threat to people trying to evacuate the site in the event of a fire
  - be constructed and arranged so that the spread of fire would be limited
  - be separated from the rest of the structure by a partition that provides a **minimum of 30 minutes' fire resistance**.
- Flammable waste materials should not be allowed to accumulate but instead be cleared away promptly to skips located outside the structure; the more waste material there is within the structure, the greater the fire loading.
- The HSE has stated in its publications that LPG is the most significant contributor to the risk of fire on construction sites and that it has been implicated in many serious fires and explosions, particularly where leaks have occurred in site accommodation. It must be stored and used in a manner that:
  - minimises the amount of LPG stored on site to that needed for immediate and short-term use
  - minimises the risk of leaks or damage to cylinders and associated equipment
  - allows leaking gas, which is heavier than air, to safely disperse.
- The storage of other highly flammable and explosive materials (such as solvents, paints, adhesives, oxygen, acetylene and petrol) must be stored in a manner that:
  - minimises the risk of leaks, which will ideally be in a well-ventilated place in the open air
  - is protected from direct sunlight
  - enables oxygen cylinders to be stored separately from LPG and acetylene cylinders.

C 02

2.9.2 Storage of waste

Most construction sites generate large quantities of rubbish and waste material that present a potential fire risk. Good housekeeping is essential.

A build up of combustible material causing a fire risk

Rubbish and waste should be cleared from site on a regular basis, if the risk of fire is to be controlled.

Skips and other waste disposal containers should **not** be placed less than 3 m away from the structure under construction or the means of escape from it. If this cannot be avoided then they must be positioned to:

- ☑ encourage the regular clearing and segregation of waste
- ☑ prevent build up of a significant fire load
- ☑ be readily available to vehicles contracted to collect and deliver skips
- ☑ be away from canopies and overhanging eaves
- ☑ against a fire-resisting wall, which is high enough to prevent fire from reaching other flammable parts of the structure
- ☑ be able to use a chute made of non-combustible materials
- ☑ restrict the amount of flammable material placed within them.

The following points should also be considered.

- ☑ Site rules should state that contractors must clear their rubbish daily, or more often if required due to the nature and volume of the rubbish created.
- ☑ Skips should be emptied or replaced before the contents represent a significant fire risk.

2.9.3 Hot work

The failure to adequately control hot work has been the cause of many construction site fires, many of them on refurbishment and maintenance jobs.

> **Hot work**
>
> An activity or process that generates flame, heat or spark and introduces a foreseeable risk of fire or explosion through a source of ignition created by tools or equipment, such as the examples shown below.
>
> - ☑ Intentional source of ignition arising from working methods with or without the use of a naked flame (for example, welding, flame-cutting, soldering, blazing, heat-stripping of paint and heat sealing of roof membrane).
> - ☑ Unintentional generation of heat or sparks, by the use of power or hand tools (for example, grinding and the use of disc cutters).

A hot-work permit scheme must be introduced to make sure that such work can be carried out in a safe and controlled environment. *(For further information on hot works refer to 2.10.)*

2.9.4 Electrical safety

Electrical installations should be professionally designed, installed, inspected and maintained. This will ensure that the installation has the required capacity to cope with the intended loads and that it will remain in a safe condition. On most sites, particularly larger ones, a regime of regular inspection and maintenance of the system will be required.

Unauthorised alterations must not be made to the distribution system. Such a move indicates that the system, as installed, no longer fully satisfies the needs of the site and that it should be upgraded, with both the design and installation carried out by competent persons.

Halogen light fittings can get very hot and cause materials near them to ignite. Historically, they have been a common source of ignition for site fires and it is good practice to only use them where other forms of task lighting are not suitable and the fire risk assessment shows that it is safe to do so.

The failure of electrical hand tools and mains-powered office equipment has also been the cause of fires. The regular testing of portable electrical appliances and hand tools (PAT testing) will confirm whether the internal insulation is breaking down or there are other defects rendering the equipment a potential fire hazard. Portable electrical equipment should be switched off and disconnected from the supply when not in use for extended periods, particularly those items that it might be tempting to leave on overnight (such as photocopiers and fax machines).

Possible causes of electrical fires are shown below.

- Overheating of poorly maintained or damaged equipment and hand tools.
- Overloading of electrical circuits.
- Overloading of electrical sockets in site accommodation.
- Accumulation of combustible rubbish alongside cables (frequently in ceiling voids) or distribution boards.
- Bypassing of circuit safety devices, rendering them inoperative.
- Fitting of the incorrect rating of fuse or residual current device (RCD).
- Unauthorised modification or tapping into of the site electrical distribution system.
- Failure to carry out the periodic testing of electrical circuits and safety devices.
- Ignition of explosive airborne particles or fumes by sparking within electrical equipment or tools.
- Accidental damage to equipment and conductors that have not been adequately protected.

For further information refer to the HSE publications.

- ***Maintaining portable electrical equipment.***
- ***Maintaining portable electric equipment in low risk environments.***

2.9.5 Heating appliances

The term *heating appliances* covers a range of equipment, ranging from wall-mounted, electric site-cabin heaters, through small, free-standing, infrared or ceramic heaters, to large, forced-air LPG heaters. The precautions that will be necessary depend upon the nature of the hazard presented by the type of heater(s) in use.

The risk of fire arises from the use of heating appliances if they are sited and installed incorrectly, inadequately maintained or are not suitable for the intended use or location.

Fuel supplies for gas-fired appliances, especially propane or butane, should be kept secured outside the building and piped in through fixed pipework. Any flexible pipework should be kept as short as possible, and used only for the final connection to the cylinder. Any room in which a gas fire is used must be fitted with a permanently open vent or louvre to enable the fire appliance to operate properly without producing excess carbon dioxide. (A window that could be closed in cold weather, for example, is not acceptable.)

Gas fires, plus the associated pipework, connections and so on, must be regularly serviced by **Gas Safe registered engineers**.

Combustible material should be kept well away from heaters and stoves. Drying wet clothing in front of, or on, heaters should be prohibited; if a drying room is needed one should be provided.

Care must be taken to see that combustible materials are not allowed to build up around such heaters. Spare cylinders must not be stored in site cabins or anywhere else where they may be subjected to being heated.

All heaters and stoves, including cookers, must be turned off at the end of the working day with the supply valve on the cylinder closed.

2.9.6 Arson

Some people take great delight in setting fire to structures under construction; don't let it happen to you. Keep your security tight.

Arson has been the suspected cause of many construction site fires and so, ideally, flammable materials should not be stored where they could be seen and set alight from outside the site boundary. Effective site security is essential to prevent arson. If necessary, consider patrols by contracted security guards and/or the use of CCTV.

Some ways to prevent arson are shown below.

- Only allow authorised people access to the site during normal working hours.
- Employ effective site security to prevent unauthorised access to the site out of normal working hours.
- Do not leave flammable materials in a place where they can be seen and set on fire from outside of the site.
- If necessary, remove flammable liquids, LPG, other gases and combustible material whilst the site is closed.

2.9.7 Bonfires

Environmental factors and/or Local Authority restrictions make the controlled burning of rubbish on site an unacceptable practice. The potential for the reuse or recycling of waste materials should always be considered. Generally bonfires are only acceptable, in limited situations, for the burning of vegetation or rubbish as part of site clearance for road building projects.

If, under exceptional circumstances, bonfires are allowed, the following requirements are necessary.

- Prior approval and the necessary permits must be obtained from the relevant authorities.
- No fire should be left unattended during working hours, or left smouldering or burning after work has ceased.
- The attendant should have a suitable fire extinguisher and have been trained in its use.
- The volume of material burnt at any time must be limited to what can be fitted into a single incinerator, typically a spent 50 gallon oil-drum that has been cleaned to remove any residue of the original content.
- Prior to burning, the waste material should be checked for hazardous items (such as empty aerosol cans and other highly flammable substances).
- They should be situated away from any buildings, boundaries, roadways, overhead lines, fuel stores or other combustible materials or structures.
- Consideration must be given to wind direction and strength, as drifting smoke could be a nuisance to others, particularly where it would become a danger to users of nearby roads by reducing visibility.

Never light a bonfire using any flammable liquid. There could be a danger to the person lighting the fire being burnt by the flash as the flammable liquid ignites and also a chance of secondary fires starting as heavier-than-air vapours spread.

2.9.8 Plant and equipment operations

Most engine-driven plant and equipment will generate heat during use; often more heat than necessary if it is poorly maintained or if it is being used beyond its design capacity. Furthermore, plant can easily represent a fire hazard when it is being refuelled or stored away, under cover, whilst still hot.

The lead-acid batteries used in plant and other vehicles give off an explosive gas when the batteries are being recharged, if the batteries are of a type where the filler caps have to be removed or loosened. The same will apply to any type of electrical equipment (for example, temporary traffic light units, which incorporate this type of battery).

2.9.9 Protection of finished surfaces

Once a building is nearing completion, it is common practice to use temporary coverings to protect finished surfaces and installed equipment during the remaining fitting-out phase. These coverings often take the form of plastic sheeting, fibreboard or similar materials, some of which may be flammable. They can consequently assist in spreading fire. Ideally, purpose-made, fire-retardant materials should be used.

If non-fire-retardant materials are used the protective covering should be fitted as late as possible in the project and the fire protection measures must be suitable to cover the enhanced risk.

2.9.10 Poor housekeeping

The accumulation of flammable waste material will increase the fire loading of any structure and has the potential to put people at risk by blocking access to fire alarms, fire-fighting equipment and escape routes.

Advice on good practice in the storage and disposal of waste is included later in this chapter.

Some other examples of poor housekeeping that increase fire risk are shown below.

- Work being carried out in designated escape routes (for example, tower scaffolds erected on staircases).
- Flammable and highly flammable liquids and gases not being returned to their proper storage areas after use.
- Access routes for the emergency services being blocked and preventing access to all parts of the site.

2.9.11 Scaffolding sheeting

If scaffolding is intended to be sheeted and used as a means of escape it must be made to a flame retardant standard. Consideration should be given to ventilation (to clear smoke) and access for the emergency services.

2.10 Hot work

Cutting, burning and welding operations, together with the use of blowlamps and other LPG-fuelled tools, have been the cause of many fires on building and construction sites. It is essential that anyone involved in hot works is:

- aware of the fire risk in the particular location where work is to be carried out
- aware of how heat might be transmitted to other areas
- trained and competent to use the equipment that will produce the source of heat
- trained and competent to select and use mobile fire extinguishers.

Precautions must be taken where heat from a work process could be transmitted to other combustible materials (for example, where hot works are carried out on steelwork or pipes adjacent to, or passing through, flammable materials, such as studwork walls or timber floors). Where this kind of operation is anticipated, it is essential that all combustible materials, including liquids, are protected before any work is allowed to start. Special care should be taken when cutting or welding is carried out above flammable materials. Precautions must be taken to prevent sparks or hot fragments of metal from dropping onto and igniting the flammable material below (such as removing it or covering it with fire-resisting material).

The following precautions must be observed when using bitumen boilers.

- ☑ The distance between the boiler and LPG cylinder must be at least three metres.
- ☑ The boiler must never be left unattended, moved or towed whilst the burner is alight.
- ☑ If possible avoid taking boilers onto roofs; if this cannot be avoided, place the boiler on a non-combustible, insulating base.
- ☑ Appropriate fire-fighting equipment must be located nearby.

Hot work should cease one hour before the site is vacated at the end of the day with the area actively monitored for signs of fire until the site is vacated or, it is recommended, two hours before the site is vacated on high risk sites (such as large, timber-frame projects), with the area actively monitored for the first hour and then checked again at the two hour point.

Checks must include an inspection of cavities, around eaves, behind studding, and so on, and into other voids where smouldering material would otherwise go undetected.

The introduction of a permit system should be considered for all hot work, except where the risk of fire is considered to be low. Hot-work permits are formal management documents that should only be issued by someone with official authority to do so.

Hot-work permits should normally include the following.

- ☑ The location where the work will be carried out.
- ☑ A description of the hot work to be carried out.
- ☑ The proposed start time and duration of the workplaces.
- ☑ The time at which the permit expires (the work must be completed or cease at that time).

Other precautions to be taken, which should be reflected in the hot-work permit, include instructions for:

- ☑ clearing all combustible material from the surrounding area
- ☑ checking for combustible material in adjacent hidden locations
- ☑ having a suitable and serviceable fire extinguisher at the place of the work
- ☑ maintaining a careful watch for the early signs of fire during the work
- ☑ protecting combustible material that cannot be cleared (for example, by the use of non-combustible matting)
- ☑ carrying out the post-work checks already mentioned.

e.g.

For an example of a hot-work permit refer to Section G: *Checklists and forms*.

Even where a formal hot-work permit scheme is in operation, because of a perceived low risk of fire, basic fire safety precautions (such as having a serviceable fire extinguisher to hand) are still required.

2.11 Flammable liquids and gases

!

You cannot be too careful when LPG is being used on your site; the person doing the job must be competent and you must ensure that they are.

LPG should be stored in purpose-designed, fireproof compounds or cages that prevent the accumulation of vapour in the event of a leak. Compounds should have a level base of compacted earth, concrete or paving slabs and be surrounded by a secure chain-link fence at least 1.8 m high. There should be sufficient shelter to prevent cylinders from being exposed to extremes of weather. Signs must be clearly displayed indicating the presence of LPG, and prohibiting smoking and the use of any naked flame in the area of the store.

Precautions for the use of LPG include:

- ☑ minimising the amount of LPG on site at any one time
- ☑ turning off cylinder valves before connecting or disconnecting any equipment
- ☑ checking cylinders and all associated equipment before use; do not use if there are signs of damage or leaks
- ☑ use soapy water to try to detect the exact location of leaks; the smell should provide the initial indication

- store LPG cylinders:
  - with their valves uppermost, apart from cylinders used to provide fuel for LPG-powered plant, which are used and stored on their side
  - away from oxygen, highly flammable liquids, oxidisers, toxic or corrosive gases or substances
  - a distance of at least three metres from other substances, although they may be kept in the same compound.

Small, easily portable LPG cylinders and canisters should ideally be removed from site after work.

LPG cylinders must never be stored in unventilated metal boxes or site accommodation.

Following mechanical failure of LPG equipment, or any other event that causes the release of LPG, the resulting gas will form a flammable mixture with air at gas concentrations between approximately 2% and 10%.

Ignition of released LPG, where the concentration exceeds 2%, can result in fire or, if confined, an explosion. If a leak does not ignite immediately, and the LPG and air mixture drifts from the point of release, it will gradually become more diluted. However, if the concentration still exceeds 2%, ignition could cause a flash or cloud-fire back to the point of release.

A leak of LPG may be noticed either by the smell or the noise of the gas escaping. There may also be condensation or frosting on the outside of the cylinder.

Leaks must not be traced with a lighted match or naked flame as this would almost certainly cause an explosion. Only soapy water or a proprietary leak-finding fluid should be used.

If it is suspected that LPG has leaked inside a building, no attempt should be made to touch any electrical apparatus.

Never turn on light switches or any other electrical equipment if a leak of LPG is suspected.

Open all doors and windows, if it is safe to do so, and leave immediately. Do not re-enter the building until advice has been sought and you are told it is safe.

All LPG cylinders and regulators for use with fixed heaters, cookers and lighting within site huts must be kept outside and the gas supply piped in using rigid copper piping. The use of flexible hosing is permitted only between the cylinders and changeover valves or manifolds, and for the final connection to appliances, but this must be kept as short as possible.

All pipework should be exposed and easy to get to for inspection, but located to prevent accidental damage. Any work on LPG pipework or other parts of a fixed installation, including testing, must only be carried out by appropriately trained (Gas Safe registered) persons.

Ventilation for heaters and cookers must be permanent and adequate. It should be divided equally between vents at high and low level.

e.g.

A two-burner cooker in a site hut needs approximately 150 mm x 150 mm ventilation. A 3 kW convector heater needs approximately 225 mm x 225 mm ventilation.

Inspections of all appliances must be carried out before use. If soot forms or smells occur, do not use or allow the appliance to be used. Find out the reasons for the problem and have it put right.

Before using LPG equipment in an enclosed space a risk assessment must be carried out. It is essential to ensure that there is adequate ventilation, which may have to be forced. This is necessary to ensure full combustion and also to make certain that the products of combustion, other fumes and excess oxygen from any cutting apparatus are removed. Enhanced fire safety precautions and the use of atmospheric monitoring should be considered.

Wherever practicable, cylinders used with operations in confined spaces should be located in a safe area, preferably in the open air. The supply pressure should be reduced to the lowest practicable level on leaving the source of supply.

Where cylinders are used below ground level, the number must be kept as small as possible. All cylinders and hoses should be removed as soon as work has finished or if it is interrupted for a substantial period (for example, overnight).

LPG cylinders must not be taken into confined spaces, as defined in the Confined Spaces Regulations, unless exceptional safety precautions are taken.

Highly flammable and explosive substances (such as adhesives, solvents and paint) should be stored as follows.

- An external, secure, purpose-built compound, where site conditions allow.
- A suitable secure, internal, fireproof storeroom where external storage is not practical, although it will be necessary to install fire detection and suppression systems.
- A metal, lockable cabinet or bin, for immediate or imminent use at the place of work.

Where it is necessary to store bulk quantities of highly flammable substance, the requirements of the storage area are shown below.

Image showing bad practice – Designated refuelling and cutting points should be used or better still another type of powered equipment when working in timber frame or enclosed buildings

- ☑ Located outdoors, apart from in exceptional circumstances, in a position where it cannot be accidentally hit by vehicles or plant.
- ☑ Have a gently sloping concrete pad with a sump to catch any leaks or spillage and a bund that is able to contain the contents of the largest can or drum stored + 10%, where bulk liquids are stored.
- ☑ Protected against direct sunlight.
- ☑ At least 2 m away from nearby buildings or boundaries, except where the boundary of the store forms part of a solid wall, cans or drums may be stacked up against that wall up to one metre from the top.
- ☑ Fitted with appropriate signage to indicate the content (such as 'highly flammable' or 'flashpoint below 32°C').
- ☑ Fitted with an 'EX' sign when an assessment under the Dangerous Substances and Explosive Atmospheres Regulations (DSEAR) indicates that an explosive atmosphere could be present in the event of a leak.
- ☑ Fitted with 'No smoking' or 'Naked flame' signs.
- ☑ Kept locked when access is not required.
- ☑ Equipped with intrinsically safe electrical circuits and fittings where electrical supplies are necessary.
- ☑ Equipped with dry powder or foam fire extinguishers.
- ☑ Equipped with a quantity of absorbent material, to soak up any spilt liquids, and a suitable container for the collection and safe disposal of the contaminated absorbent.
- ☑ If necessary, equipped with racking made from a non-ferrous metal or other non-combustible material.

Ex icon hazard sign

The secure storage of dangerous materials in a proper compound or cabinet is as equally important as using them in a safe manner.

If for any reason it is not practical to store highly flammable or other dangerous substances outside (for example, if the footprint of the structure under construction completely fills the land available), conditions for outdoor storage above apply, and the DSEAR assessment must consider whether the risks of storage indoors are acceptable. If not, safe, off-site storage and transportation must be arranged.

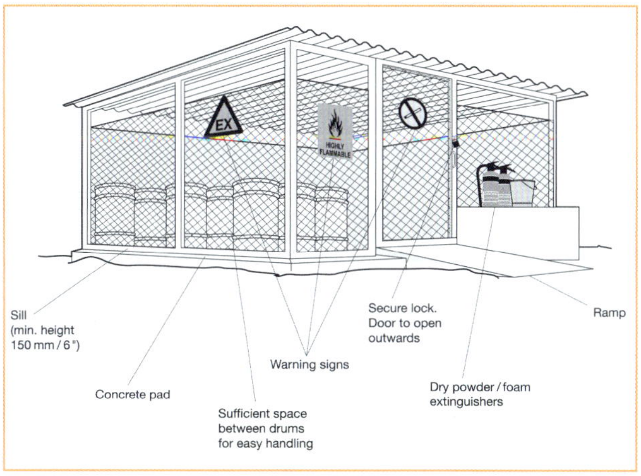

A secure dangerous substances storage area

In deciding whether or not the risks associated with indoor storage are acceptable, it is likely that expert advice will be required to determine the suitability of the proposed storage area with regard to its fire and explosion resistance.

It is recommended that the maximum quantities that may be stored in cabinets and bins are no more than 50 litres for highly flammable liquids (and flammable liquids with a flashpoint below the maximum ambient temperature of the workroom/working area) and no more than 250 litres for other flammable liquids with a higher flashpoint of up to 55°C.

Under no circumstances should storage areas be located underground as this would prevent the dispersal of heavier-than-air vapours, should a leak occur.

When not in use, containers of flammable liquids needed for current work should be kept closed and stored in suitable cabinets or bins of fire-resisting construction, designed to retain spills (110% volume of the largest vessel normally stored in it).

All signs must conform to the Health and Safety (Safety Signs and Signals) Regulations.

When storing materials at the workplace, ready for use, only store one day's supply, or less, where highly flammable materials are to be used.

On many sites there will be a need to store bulk quantities of vehicle fuels, particularly diesel oil, usually in a bowser or drum. If storage drums are used, the same conditions apply as for the storage of other highly flammable and explosive substances.

Carelessly dispensing fuel into vehicles or plant when the engine is still hot has been the cause of many serious fires and injuries.

Where fuel oil is to be dispensed into containers or vehicles, the outlet must be fitted with a valve or nozzle, which closes automatically when not in use and cannot be fixed in the open position unless an automatic cut-off nozzle is used on the end of the hose.

The hose and nozzle should be housed in an enclosed, secure cabinet with a drip tray when not in use, or have a lockable valve where the feed leaves the tank. Hoses should be kept locked or kept within the bund when not in use.

Any permanent valve or tap that opens directly from the tank must:

- be located within the secondary containment system (bund wall)
- discharge vertically downwards
- be locked off when not in use.

Finally, no vent must discharge outside of the bund in the event of an overfill.

Generally, petrol is only used in relatively low quantities for small generators and some hand tools (such as chainsaws) but, however small the quantity, it must be stored safely. Petrol will usually be stored in 20 litre metal jerry cans or five-litre, purpose-made plastic containers. The jerry cans or containers must be kept closed, except for when the content is being decanted.

The positioning of fire extinguisher points, and the types of extinguisher, must be based in part upon where construction materials, flammable substances and gases will be stored and used.

The positioning of the stores for flammable substances and gas bottles should be such that any fire in the vicinity would not prevent the use of an emergency escape route, thereby forcing people past the hazard.

2.12 Higher risk projects

Projects that may require extra precautions could be timber-frame structures, multistorey buildings or high rise construction sites, larger projects or those where significant risks have been identified on the risk assessment. Some of these are explained in more detail below.

2.12.1 Timber-frame structures

There have been recent significant fires involving large, timber-frame buildings under construction, including Peckham, Camberwell and Basingstoke, which all resulted in fire damage to adjacent buildings. Large, timber-frame buildings under construction pose a significant risk to fire-fighters, construction workers and members of the public.

The use of timber-frame as a method of construction, together with other innovative construction products and techniques has increased markedly in recent years, as a popular alternative to traditional building construction methods. However, it has demonstrated how devastating construction site fires can be, not only with regard to the potential loss of life and the total destruction of the structure itself, but also the major fire damage that can be caused to other properties over a wide area.

As such structures are at their most vulnerable when the timber structure is being erected and before any cladding or protective skins are installed each structure should be clad at the earliest practical opportunity. Designers should give consideration to the use of materials that have been given a fire protective or retardant treatment.

Ideally, large timber-frame structures will be compartmentalised at the earliest opportunity to prevent the spread of fire and to ensure a safe travel distance for anyone who has to evacuate the structure in an emergency.

High risk timber-frame buildings require additional fire prevention measures

Consideration must be given to using fire-resistant boarding to temporarily fire-stop ducts and shafts until the permanent fire-engineered solution is installed.

Temporary or permanent fire-resisting doors, panels and fire stopping should be installed as early in the construction programme as is practical.

Where there are multiple, timber-frame structures on a site, the fire risk assessment must consider how a fire in one of them could be prevented or slowed from spreading to the others or to adjacent premises. To this end, temporary non-combustible cladding could be used to cover exposed timber and other combustible construction materials prior to the final cladding being installed.

www.

The UK Timber Frame Association has published five guides (freely downloadable from its website) related to fire safety in timber-frame construction, as part of their safe site strategy.

- ☑ ***Risk assessment checklist.***
- ☑ ***Separating distance guidance.***
- ☑ ***Site safe registration/compliant.***
- ☑ ***Guidance notes on wireless fire alarms.***
- ☑ ***16 steps to fire safety on timber-frame construction sites.***

For examples of major timber-frames and investigation into the risks and causes refer to the timber-frame fires website.

2.12.2 Multistorey buildings

It is advisable that the FRS are informed where work will take place above 18 m, as specialist access equipment may be required.

This type of structure, during either construction or refurbishment, can pose particular problems with regard to the management of fire risk. Incomplete or absent fire-engineered solutions can result in the rapid spread of fire, leaving any workers on the upper floors particularly at risk. Furthermore, it is possible that in some circumstances it will not be practical to supply sufficient water for fire-fighting purposes to the higher levels.

In these circumstances a specific risk assessment must be undertaken to establish how the safety of those working on the upper levels can be assured in the event of a fire.

Designers have a major part to play in maintaining fire safety, not only in the selection of materials and the work methods that are necessary as a result of design decisions, but also in ensuring that the following.

- ☑ Temporary, fire-resistant compartmentalisation or other fire-engineering solutions are incorporated as necessary until permanent fire stopping is in place.
- ☑ With new-build or refurbished premises, a working fire alarm system 'follows the building up' so that it can be heard in all parts of the building at all stages of construction.
- ☑ The fire alarm system is electrically operated (hard-wired or wireless) with break-glass call points and sounders at each level.
- ☑ The rising water main(s) are installed and commissioned at an early stage before interior work starts.
- ☑ If some floors are already occupied, the risk assessment and fire emergency plans allow for:
  - the integration of the fire alarm systems for both the construction areas and the occupied floors
  - any restrictions that prevent construction workers accessing the occupied part of the building, particularly escape routes
  - the possibility that construction workers may not be allowed access to occupied parts of the building.
- ☑ Access to all staircases, or other protected routes, is maintained at all times, as far as possible.
- ☑ One staircase designated as a fire-fighting staircase for the sole use of the fire and rescue service during an emergency.
- ☑ Fire doors with self-closers are fitted to protect the escape stairways and adequate fire stopping.

2.13 Classes of fire

All fires can be placed into one of the following six categories.

1. **Class A.** Carbonaceous material (such as paper, cloth, wood and rubber) often referred to as solid fuel fires.
2. **Class B.** Flammable liquids or liquefiable solids (such as oil, fat, paint and fuel). These can be subdivided into:
   - **B1.** Fires involving liquids that are soluble in water (such as methanol). They can be extinguished by carbon dioxide, dry powder and water spray
   - **B2.** Fires involving liquids that are not soluble in water (such as petrol and oil). They can be extinguished using foam, carbon dioxide and dry powder.
3. **Class C.** Flammable gases or liquefied gases (such as propane, butane, hydrogen or acetylene).
4. **Class D.** Combustible metals (such as magnesium, sodium and phosphorus).
5. **Electrical fires.** Any fire involving electrical apparatus or equipment.
6. **Class F.** High temperature cooking oils or fats (such as those used in deep fat fryers in large catering establishments or restaurants).

C
02

2.13.1 Class A. Carbonaceous material

On the majority of building or construction sites, the following carbonaceous items are freely available sources of fuel.

- Cardboard, paper and cloth.
- Wood.
- Dirty rags, oily rags and clothes.
- Packaging materials.

If a fire occurs involving carbonaceous material, a hose reel or a water extinguisher should be used. The jet of water should be aimed at the base of the fire first, and then moved progressively over the whole of the burning area. Always remove the material from the source of heat if possible, but without endangering the person involved or starting a fire in another location.

2.13.2 Class B. Flammable liquids or liquefiable solids

Includes any fire involving flammable liquids (some examples are shown below).

- Petrol or diesel.
- Oil.
- Paraffin.
- Paint.
- Resin and adhesive.

This type of fire should be dealt with using foam or dry powder extinguishers, depending on whether the fire is contained or flowing.

If the fire is contained, use a foam extinguisher with the jet of foam directed at the back of the container. This allows a blanket of foam to build up and spread across the surface of the burning liquid.

If the fire is flowing, a dry powder extinguisher should be directed at the front edge of the fire, in an attempt to separate the flames from the fuel.

The aim of using extinguishers in such a way is for the fire to be covered with a blanket of either foam or dry powder. This will cut off the supply of air, and thus the oxygen, to the fire.

Once the blanket has been laid, do not disturb it until the liquid has cooled. Any reintroduction of air may cause the fire to re-ignite.

Never use a water extinguisher or a hose reel on a fire involving any flammable liquid. The water will react violently with the burning liquid and cause an explosion.

2.13.3 Class C. Flammable and liquefied gases

Extreme caution is necessary when dealing with fires involving liquefied gases as there will always be the danger of an explosion.

LPG expands to a ratio of 274:1 so a leak of just one litre of liquid would produce a cloud of gas, if diluted in air to the right concentration, large enough to fill a room 3 m x 2 m x 2 m. This would cause an explosive atmosphere.

If a fire occurs in which a compressed gas cylinder is directly involved the following actions should be taken.

- Call the FRS and tell them the location of the cylinders and type of gas involved.
- Attempt to turn the gas off at the cylinder, if it is safe to do so.
- Attempt to turn off any gas appliances, if it is safe to do so.
- Activate the emergency evacuation procedure and clear the site.

Do not try to fight a fire in which a compressed gas cylinder is directly involved; leave it to the FRS as an overheated cylinder can explode.

If a fire involves other combustible materials (for example, timber that might cause the fire to spread to the location of the cylinders) a decision based upon personal safety will have to be taken on whether to attempt to fight the fire to prevent an escalation of the situation.

Class C fires are best dealt with by the use of dry powder extinguishers.

2.13.4 Class D. Combustible metals

Fires of this type involve magnesium, sodium, phosphorus and similar metals, and should only be dealt with by trained fire fighters.

Never apply water to any burning metal fire or a fire involving powered metal. It would cause an immediate explosive reaction.

Specially formulated powders are available for use in controlling fire in metals but, as a last resort, if no proprietary powder is available dry sand or earth may be applied to smother the burning area.

The proprietary powder should be carefully placed and not thrown onto the burning metal. Throwing the powder will cause the burning material to spread.

Be sure either to wear darkened safety glasses whilst attempting to cover the fire, or to look away from the extreme brightness. Failure to take these precautions could damage the eyes.

2.13.5 Electrical fires

Fires involving electrical equipment can be dealt with using carbon dioxide (CO_2) or dry powder. In staff training, the following simple rules for safety should be emphasised.

- Do not use water on any fire involving electrical equipment. You may be electrocuted.
- Switch off the electricity supply, if possible, before fighting the fire. It is then just an ordinary fire.
- Do not approach closer than one metre to any fire where the electrical supply has not been switched off.
- CO_2 is the best extinguishing medium if the concentration of gas can be confined (for example, within an electrical distribution cupboard).
- In extinguishing electrical fires, direct the discharge from the extinguisher to one edge of the fire and, with a sweeping movement, pass to the far edge until the fire has been extinguished.

Electrical equipment used on building and construction sites sometimes incorporates devices to protect against overheating and fire.

Most fires in electrical equipment are due to misuse or neglect where appliances have not been properly maintained or are being used for a purpose, or in a manner, for which they were not designed.

A fuse larger than the appliance rating will negate the purpose of the fuse and render the appliance potentially unsafe.

All staff should be properly trained so that they do not misuse equipment, and ensure that damaged or defective equipment is reported, taken out of use and professionally repaired.

2.13.6 Class F. Cooking oils

Class F fires are fires involving cooking oils or fats. Class F fires differ from conventional liquid fires due to the high temperatures involved.

These types of fire have auto ignition temperatures in excess of 340°C. They are very difficult to extinguish using conventional extinguishers with a Class B capability, where other flammable liquids (for example, petrol) have a low flash point and so auto ignition temperatures make them easier to extinguish.

Extinguishers designed for cooking oil fires typically include wet chemical, dry chemical, or foam based with special additives. These special materials react with the hot burning oil to create a thick, soapy, heat-resistant crust, on top of the cooking oil surface, preventing the flammable vapours from reacting with oxygen. This reaction is called saponification. The alkalinity of the extinguishing material quickly reacts with the burning oil to create the soap layer.

Due to the high heat, using an incorrect extinguisher on these fires can be extremely dangerous. Some reasons for this are given below.

- A water jet extinguisher directed at the surface of burning cooking oil will create an explosion. The water is quickly converted into steam, resulting in the possible expulsion of burning oil, which could spread the fire and harm the person using the extinguisher.
- Conventional foam extinguishers can extinguish the flame, but the heat involved quickly destroys the foam blanket, exposing the surface of the oil and allowing re-ignition.
- Carbon dioxide and powder extinguishers are effective in extinguishing the flame, but without sealing the surface of the liquid from oxygen the oil will rapidly re-ignite.
- Conventional powder, foam or CO_2 extinguishers are normally too powerful and direct. They can easily splash the burning liquid and spread the fire.

2.13.7 Other types of fire

2.13.7.1 Flammable adhesives and flammable liquid stores

For fires of this type use dry powder or foam.

Extreme care must be taken if the adhesive is petroleum or spirit-based as explosive vapours will be given off.

2.13.7.2 Cooking ranges

For fires involving cooking ranges use foam, dry powder, CO_2 or a fire blanket. Never move a burning saucepan or chip pan from a cooker. The contents may splash and cause serious burns.

2.13.7.3 Petrol and diesel in stores

For fires involving petrol or diesel in stores use foam or dry powder.

2.13.7.4 Petrol or diesel-powered plant

For fires involving petrol or diesel-powered plant use foam or dry powder.

2.13.7.5 Hot work with cutting or welding equipment and bitumen boilers

For fires of this type use foam, dry powder or CO_2. Turn off the heater. The correct types of fire extinguisher must be provided and kept close at hand, with a careful watch being maintained for fire breaking out whilst work is in progress.

2.14 Fire-fighting equipment

2.14.1 Portable fire extinguishers

Fire extinguishers do not prevent fires. However, they can be used by trained employees in an attempt to minimise loss and damage after a fire has started. It goes without saying that preventing the fire in the first place is a far better option.

A good fire point on site

Where there is a realistic possibility that staff will have to use fire extinguishers, they should be trained in their use. Fire safety law requires that an appropriate number of staff are trained in the selection and use of fire extinguishers. Even though staff may be trained, some companies may take the view that all staff should simply evacuate the structure and leave fire-fighting to the professionals.

In line with the risks identified in a fire risk assessment, adequate numbers of suitable types of portable fire extinguisher must be provided and kept available throughout the premises.

Extinguishers must be located in clearly visible locations near exits on each floor. They should be fixed to the wall with their carrying handles approximately one metre above the floor level. Where this is not possible, they should be fixed in position (for example, using base plates or stands) at floor level.

In the open, extinguishers should be situated in red painted boxes, which are either sitting on the floor or raised 500 mm above ground level, with a 'Fire point' sign at a height readily seen above any obstructions. Care must be taken during winter months to ensure that extinguisher contents do not freeze.

To protect electrical distribution panels and items of electrical equipment, appropriate extinguishers (usually carbon dioxide) must be provided near but not dangerously close to the equipment concerned.

For large or costly items of equipment (such as computer suites) the installation of automatic fire detection and extinguishing systems should be considered.

2.14.1.1 Colour coding of fire extinguishers

It is essential that staff who may be called upon to use a fire extinguisher have been trained in their use and have a clear understanding of the colour coding system. All fire extinguishers are painted red with a contrasting colour somewhere on the casing (such as a contrasting panel or handle), which indicates what extinguishing agent the extinguisher contains.

Colour coding enables a trained person to rapidly identify the type of extinguisher needed in an emergency. The coloured panels must not cover more than 5% of the surface area.

Extinguishing medium	**Water:** for wood, paper, textile and solid material fires	**Foam:** for liquid fires	**Powder:** for liquid and electrical fires	**Carbon dioxide:** for liquid and electrical fires	**Wet chemical:** for wood, paper, textile, cooking oil and solid material fires
Colour of panel	Red 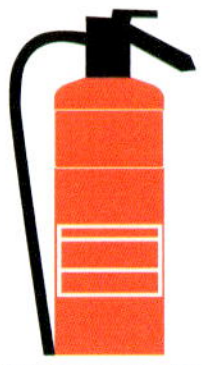	Cream 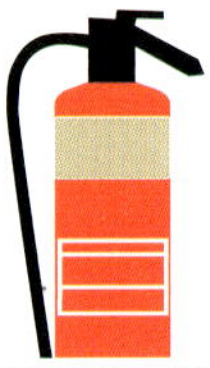	Blue 	Black 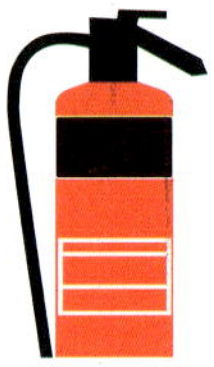	Yellow 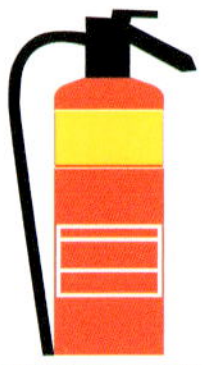
Where not to use	**Do not** use on liquid, electrical or metal fires	**Do not** use on electrical or metal fires	**Do not** use on metal fires	**Do not** use on metal fires	**Do not** use on liquid, gas or electrical fires

Note: dry powder extinguishers may be provided in addition to or substituted for water, foam or carbon dioxide extinguishers. Extinguishers used to control Class B fires will not work on Class F fires because of the high temperatures generated.

A few extinguishers may still be in use that complied with a much earlier standard of colour coding. This standard required that the whole body of each extinguisher was painted in the same contrasting colours that are now used in the later standard. In addition, a small number of extinguishers are bright silver or self-coloured metal with a designated panel stating the medium they contain. The colour coding of the panel is the same as that listed above.

www.

For further information on using the correct type of fire extinguisher refer to *Fire safety in construction* (HSG168).

2.14.1.2 Inspection and maintenance

Fire-fighting equipment should be inspected monthly and maintained and tested at least once a year by a competent person. The maintenance and tests should be carried out in accordance with the manufacturer's instructions.

Extinguishers should be tested by discharge at intervals specified in BS 5306, and always be recharged immediately after any use. The maintenance and inspection of fire-fighting equipment should be recorded in a register.

2.14.1.3 Hazardous vapours from fire extinguishers

The discharge of a carbon dioxide (CO_2) extinguisher in any small, enclosed or confined space will reduce the percentage of oxygen in the air. The dust cloud from a dry powder extinguisher may, in a confined space, produce local and temporary breathing difficulties and poor visibility.

Once an extinguisher has been discharged in such circumstances, the user should leave the area immediately. When it is safe to do so, the area should be thoroughly ventilated before allowing anyone to re-enter. If there is a need to re-enter before the air has cleared, suitable breathing apparatus will have to be worn.

2.14.1.4 Staff training in the selection and use of fire extinguishers

There is a legal requirement for employers to ensure that all employees are familiar with fire procedures, and that an appropriate number of employees are trained in the use of fire-fighting equipment. Training in the selection and use of portable extinguishers is essential if they are to be used effectively in fighting small fires. It is also very important that the right type of extinguisher is used on certain types of fire.

Attention should be given to the physical strength of persons who may have to use extinguishers. Some extinguishers weigh 20 kg.

During staff training on the use of extinguishers, the following points also need to be emphasised.

- Think of evacuation first.
- Only use an extinguisher if it is safe for you to do so.
- Do not let the fire come between you and your escape route. You may become trapped if the fire develops.
- If the extinguisher does not appear to be working or is ineffective on the fire, get out immediately.
- If the fire starts to increase or gets out of control, get out immediately.

During induction training or ongoing staff training, the following points should be made to all staff.

- Do not use a fire extinguisher unless you have been trained to do so.
- Do not misuse fire extinguishers.
- Do not move fire extinguishers from their allocated positions (for example, do not use fire extinguishers as door stops).
- Immediately report any fire extinguishers that appear to have been used, misused or damaged.

2.14.2 Hose reels

Hose reels linked to a constant water supply may sometimes be available, and can be an effective means of fire-fighting. They are more likely to be found in a live state on projects where premises are being refurbished and, if trained staff are available, they are a very useful aid in fighting some fires.

On new build projects or where the water supply to existing hose reels has been drained, it is good practice to make the supply live as the fire loading of the structure increases, providing trained staff are available.

Training employees in the correct use of hose reels is essential if fire-fighting is to be effective. Staff need to be fully aware of how the hose reels work, and what type of fire they would be effective on before they use them in an emergency.

A hose reel must not be used on:

- live electrical apparatus
- any fire involving fat, oil, paint or other flammable liquids
- any fire involving burning metal or metal powder.

To do so could lead to electrocution, or a violent explosion of burning liquid or metal.

2.14.3 Fire blankets

Fire blankets are usually sufficient to deal with small, contained fires involving tea-making facilities, frying pans and so on, and are usually found next to cooking facilities. Training in the use of a fire blanket is desirable, if not entirely necessary, because to fight a small fire using one involves actually approaching the fire and so it is far better that practice is gained during training.

Before attempting to extinguish such fires, the electricity or gas supply must be turned off.

The blanket must be pulled from its container with the corners wrapped around the hands of the person using it, making sure that their hands and forearms are completely covered. The blanket must be held at chest level and gently placed over the burning container to exclude the air from the fire.

The blanket must not be thrown because it may miss the burning container or cause it to spill, spreading the fire.

The blanket must be left in place until the container has cooled down. It is essential that no-one lifts a corner to check if the fire is out as this may allow enough air in to reignite the fire. The container must not be moved before it is cold.

C 02

2.15 Temporary accommodation units

In the drive to get the project built, it is easy to overlook the potential fire risks of the site accommodation.

Temporary accommodation units (TAUs) include site offices, canteens, rest rooms, drying rooms and toilets. They are often of timber construction, with fire-resisting surface materials. From site to site they will range from a single site cabin, combining the functions of office and canteen, to a range of single-storey, interlinked units, or they may form a multi-floor administrative complex.

The Confederation of Fire Protection Association Europe provides guidance on the fire protection of temporary buildings on construction sites, covering fire risks, fire protection requirements for escape and protection against the spread of fire.

Information on the *Guidance on fire safety in construction* (HSG168) is available from the HSE and guidance on the recommended frequencies for the inspection and testing of most electrical installations in temporary buildings is available from the Institute of Engineering and Technology.

2.15.1 Location of temporary accommodation units

A fire risk assessment will help determine the correct location, siting and use of a TAU.

TAUs should be located in the open air and separated from the building under construction and storage compounds by a fire break of at least 6 m (20 m on timber frame and other high risk sites). If such separation is not possible, the risk of fire spreading can be reduced if the TAU or the adjacent part of the structure is fire resisting to a minimum of 30 minutes. For TAUs that are located inside the building under construction, their fire resistance needs more careful consideration and they must include a fitted fire detection system. Under no circumstances should they be located in timber-frame structures.

TAUs should be designed and constructed:

- of materials that would not contribute significantly to the growth of a fire or the propagation of smoke or corrosive fumes
- of fire-resisting material to BS 476 with regard to walls, roof, doors and windows, to achieve 30 minutes' fire resistance
- where stacked vertically, the floor and roof assembly, and members supporting it, should have at least a 30 minute fire resistance.

Where TAUs do not sit flush on the ground, measures must be taken to prevent the accumulation of rubbish in the space beneath the floor, a gap which will also enhance under-floor ventilation.

For an example of a completed fire risk assessment for temporary accommodation units refer to Appendix A.

2.15.2 Sleeping accommodation

Sleeping accommodation could include facilities provided on site or a separate caravan site provided solely for the use of the construction project. This accommodation needs a specific fire risk assessment.

If caravans are to be used they must be spaced in accordance with the Local Authority's requirements, and the necessary fire alarm and fire-fighting equipment must be provided.

2.15.3 Fire alarm systems

The fire alarm system for TAUs will inevitably vary between sites. For a single or double site cabin set-up, a verbal shout of 'fire' would be acceptable providing it can be heard throughout the site in normal circumstances. Where a fire could remain undetected for a period of time, smoke alarms should be installed.

The more TAUs there are, which will be generally indicative of bigger sites, the more sophisticated the alarm system should be. For small TAU complexes, a hand-operated fire bell might be sufficient providing it is audible throughout the complex. For larger complexes and areas where cooking is carried out, an electrical break-glass system with multiple call points and sounders may be required.

For TAUs that are within the building under construction, the TAU fire alarm should be integrated as for the rest of the building.

Fire alarm systems should be tested weekly to confirm that they are audible throughout the complex. Where multiple call points are installed, they should be used in rotation for the purpose of testing the system. Test records should be maintained.

Consideration should be given to fitting automatic fire detection systems and intruder alarms to temporary buildings where flammable substances are stored.

2.15.4 Means of escape

For single and double cabin set-up, the means of escape will generally be obvious and special considerations will not be necessary. Ideally in all TAU complexes, there will be escape routes in at least two different directions from all points within the complex.

If, in places, there is only one escape route:

- it must be adequately protected from fire so that it will always be available, if needed
- any high risk equipment or materials must not be located adjacent to it
- it is likely that specialist advice will be necessary to assess travel distances and the capacity of the escape route to handle the maximum number of people who would have to use it.

Fire escape routes can be blocked unintentionally

Needless to say, all escape routes must be kept clear of obstructions that are likely to hinder an emergency evacuation.

Employers (or the responsible person) must have regard for the requirements of the Disability Discrimination Act when considering means of escape.

They should also consider the following points.

- As part of emergency planning, dedicated escape routes should be decided on, clearly signed and adequately lit.
- All directional signs should be clearly visible, kept unobstructed and conform to the Health and Safety (Safety Signs and Signals) Regulations.
- Such signs should be positioned where the escape route changes direction or level. The signs must indicate the final exit to a place of safety.

2.15.5 Fire-fighting equipment

All TAUs should be equipped with hand-held fire extinguishers as a minimum. The appropriate type of extinguisher will depend upon what the fuel for any fire would be (some examples are shown below).

- Water fire extinguishers should be provided where the fuel is likely to be paper, cardboard, timber and so on.
- Carbon dioxide extinguishers will be required where there is a significant amount of electrical equipment (such as computer terminals, server and photocopier rooms).
- Dry powder extinguishers will be required where there is a significant quantity of flammable liquids.
- A fire blanket will be required in any TAU where cooking oils are heated (such as kitchens and canteens).

Fire extinguishers should only be used by people who have been trained. Even then, they must always have at least one route of escape available to them in case fire-fighting has to be abandoned; they must also be capable of making that decision.

2.15.6 Emergency evacuation

In the event of a fire, the first priority is to get everyone out of the TAUs and account for them. How difficult this will be depends upon the size of the TAU complex, how many people are involved and whether they have full mobility. Visitors must also be accounted for.

Toxic smoke is the main cause of fatalities in premises fires, which makes it a greater hazard in enclosed office-complex fires than for fires that occur in the open air. Prompt evacuation is paramount.

Everyone must know their designated assembly point and what to do when they get there. The appointment of fire wardens will assist in confirming that no-one remains in larger TAU complexes following evacuations.

Periodically practising emergency evacuations (fire drills) will give some idea of how effective the emergency evacuation plan is and whether further work on it must be done.

No-notice practice evacuations are the most accurate way of assessing how effective the evacuation plan is. However, it is accepted that operational reasons may make these impractical.

Where construction site offices are located in a multiple-occupancy building, the safety of other occupiers, as well as their visitors and members of the public, must be a consideration. For example, emergency exit routes from the premises may have to be maintained or provided for other occupiers through the construction area or other provisions made for their safety.

2.15.7 Location of occupants

In larger office complexes, it may be necessary to appoint fire wardens whose job it is to ensure that offices and other accommodation are completely evacuated in the event of the fire alarm sounding (including practice drills) and to conduct a roll call at the assembly point.

The fire wardens must be trained in their duties and have a clear understanding of the area of the complex for which they are responsible.

The number of fire wardens required will depend on several factors, including the area and layout of the office complex and the number of levels it comprises.

The location and number of staff can be identified by the use of an in/out board, signing in/out book or swipe card system that can be taken to or accessed at the assembly point and used for the roll call.

Arrangements must be made for visitors to be logged into and out of offices so that, in the case of an emergency, they can be located quickly and escorted to a safe place.

2.15.8 Emergency lighting

Emergency lighting should always be considered when assessing the fire safety requirements for satisfactory means of escape.

If the lighting circuits fail, a standby emergency lighting system must switch on automatically and clearly illuminate:

- exits and directional signs
- corridors and associated exits
- circulation areas
- changes in levels
- any projections and protrusions (such as temporary partitioning, office equipment and storage)
- internal and external staircases.

Emergency lighting, whether by battery, standby generator or a combination of both, should be tested on a regular basis by a competent person.

Records of tests of the emergency lighting equipment should be kept and must be available for inspection when required.

2.15.9 Calling the fire and rescue service

If a fire is discovered, everyone within the TAUs must be aware of it and the FRS must be called. Where there is a switchboard, it is usual for the switchboard operator to be nominated as the person who always makes the call. However, with virtually everyone now carrying a mobile phone, it is common for several calls to be made to the emergency services about the same incident, which is preferable to everyone assuming that someone else has made the call.

Anyone calling the FRS should give the full postal address of the site and any geographical features that will assist them in locating it. It may be necessary to give further instruction if the site has more than one entrance, particularly if one has been nominated for access by the emergency services.

Even if the site has a fire alarm that is automatically connected to the FRS via an alarm company, an emergency telephone call must still be made to confirm that the automatic call has been received.

2.16 Training

You cannot expect people to react effectively in emergency situations unless they have been told what to do.

The **responsible person** must ensure that employees are provided with adequate safety training, which includes suitable and sufficient instruction and training on the appropriate precautions and actions to be taken by employees in order to safeguard themselves and other relevant persons on the premises. The training delivered must take account of the significant findings of the fire risk assessment and the emergency procedures, and be easily understandable and repeated periodically. The training should cover the following.

- Discovering a fire.
- How to raise the alarm.
- What to do on hearing the alarm.
- The procedure for alerting visitors and all staff.
- Calling the fire service.
- Evacuation procedures, assembly points and fire drills.
- The location and use of fire-fighting equipment.
- The location of escape routes.
- How to open escape doors.
- The importance of fire doors.
- How to stop equipment and isolate power.
- Not using lifts.
- The use and risks of highly flammable and explosive substances.
- Good housekeeping.
- Smoking policy and smoking areas.

Appendix A – Example of a fire risk assessment for temporary accommodation units

Record of significant findings

Risk assessment for	Assessment undertaken
Single storey site accommodation comprising five interlinked cabins Site address: *Premier Place, Carrow Road, Anytown*	Date: *3rd January 2013* Completed by: *Chris Hughton (Site manager)* Signature: *C Hughton*
Part of temporary accommodation units (TAUs) covered, if not whole area as identified above: *N/A*	This area is used for: *General office work* *Meeting room and inductions* *Canteen* *Toilets, changing and drying room*

Step 1. Identify the fire hazards

Sources of ignition	Sources of fuel	Sources of oxygen
Electrical appliances and office equipment *Electrical heater units* *Cleaning chemicals if mixed*	*Overheating/electrical failure* *Office furniture and equipment* *Project paperwork and drawings*	*None above ambient level*

Step 2. Identify the people at risk

Office-based and visiting site staff, workers in canteen and toilets and other visitors

It is NOT considered likely that the work carried out within the office accommodation could pose any risk of harm to anyone outside the site boundary (12 m away)

Step 3. Evaluate, remove, reduce and protect from risk

(3.1) Evaluate the risk of the fire occurring	*Meeting room sometimes used for storing used packaging material prior to disposal* *Desks too close to electric heaters in project office* *Chairs or clothes too close to electrical heaters in canteen*
(3.2) Evaluate the risk to people from a fire starting in the premises	*A fire in the meeting room could be undetected for some time* *A fire in the canteen on ground floor could prevent access to the rear emergency exit* *Otherwise, emergency evacuation not considered to be problematic*
(3.3) Remove and reduce the hazards that may cause a fire	*Improved housekeeping required to prevent accumulation of flammable waste materials* *Furniture to be re-arranged – requires relocation of telephone connection point* *Drying room has enclosed oil covered heaters with hooks for drying clothes – emphasise during induction* *Fit cages around electrical fires in canteen*
(3.4) Remove and reduce the risks to people from a fire	*When the defects noted above have been rectified, the existing fire precautions will be considered to be adequate* *It is noted that the fire extinguishers are due inspection in early April 2013*

Assessment review

Review due before	Completed by	Signature
3rd August 2013		

Review outcome (where substantial changes have occurred a new record sheet should be used)

Fire action plan

Will this risk assessment result in a fire action plan being drawn up? YES / ~~NO~~
Delete as applicable

For a fire risk assessment template refer to Section G: *Checklists and forms.*

03
Electrical safety

Contents

Supporting information

G: Checklists and forms

C 03

Overview

This chapter highlights the dangers associated with working on or near to live electrical circuits and the good working practices that must be adopted to ensure that such work can be carried out safely.

Each year the presence of electricity is the cause of deaths and injuries, mainly burns, on construction sites. Furthermore, over the years electricity has been a contributory factor to the starting of several fires on construction sites.

3.1 Introduction

Electricity can be regarded as a hidden killer. Unlike other hazards, in most cases, it cannot be seen, felt, smelt or heard; it may not become obvious that a cable is live until someone touches it. There may be occasional circumstances where the hum from a transformer or the noise from a motor running indicates that at least some circuits are live, but relying upon this as a risk control measure is certainly not a safe method of working.

A risk of electrocution on site could be created from any of the following.

- Contact with live parts of the electrical distribution system in the structure under construction being renovated or otherwise worked upon, and associated site accommodation.
- Contact with overhead power lines.
- Contact with underground cables.
- The use of defective electrical equipment, including hand tools.

The dangers associated with overhead power lines, underground cables and electrical hand tools are covered in other chapters of this book.

The presence of live electrical cables may not be obvious; cables inside partition walls or other hidden voids are just waiting for the unwary to accidentally damage them resulting in serious injury or even death. About three workers are electrocuted each year during refurbishment work on commercial and domestic buildings.

The temporary electrical distribution systems found on site tend to operate in a harsh environment and must be treated with care and respect.

The HSE regard refurbishment work in buildings as presenting the highest risk. Many of the accidents resulting from such work arise out of the following.

- Confusion and lack of communication as to what circuits have been made dead.
- Hitting cables buried underground, hidden by wall coverings, in voids, and so on.
- Workers, who have not been trained, knowingly working on live equipment.

Electric shock may not be the only consequence of live electrical circuits; a fault within a circuit or equipment can result in heating or sparking, which have the potential to ignite flammable materials, causing a fire or explosion as well as disrupting services to adjacent properties.

An electrical safety poster should be prominently displayed in a number of locations, if necessary. It should show basic first-aid procedures for treating someone who has received an electric shock at work.

There should be somebody on site who is trained in first aid.

3.2 Important points

- No-one other than a qualified electrician must install, maintain or alter the site distribution system.
- Electrical safety must be covered during site induction and refresher training, where it must be emphasised that unauthorised alteration to, or extension of, the site electrical distribution system will not be tolerated.
- Ideally, apart from mains-powered (230/240 volt) equipment in site offices, all other electrically powered equipment (such as electrical hand tools) should be run off a 110 volt supply.
- The power supply for 230/240 volt equipment must be fed through a safety device in addition to a fuse (for example, a residual current device (RCD)). Fuses only protect equipment; they do not 'blow' quickly enough to prevent an electric shock.
- The reason behind any safety device tripping, apart from deliberate testing, must be investigated, if necessary by bringing in a qualified electrician; attempts to reset a tripped safety device must not be made until this has been carried out.

- Work on or near to live, exposed conductors poses an obvious danger. Competence is required and such work must only be carried out under a formal permit to work.
- Electrical circuits must be tested periodically by a competent person.
- Safety devices (such as RCDs) must be tested frequently by the user.
- A permit to work system must be introduced and enforced for higher risk work (for example, where a danger from exposed live electrical wires or equipment exists).

3.3 Electricity at Work Regulations

The regulations are concerned with the safety of electrical installations and as such the details, in the main, are technical and not of general interest to site management staff, providing they have employed competent contractors to carry out electrical work. However, there are some requirements within the regulations (shown below) which, if contravened, would require addressing.

- Working on or near to live electrical parts can only be carried out where:
  - it is unreasonable in the circumstances to make the live parts dead (for example, testing could not be carried out if it was not live)
  - it is reasonable in the circumstances to allow live working (there is no other way of doing the job)
  - suitable safety precautions (for example, trained workers, a permit to work and **no** lone-working) are in place.
- Electrical equipment, which may be exposed to hostile environments or mechanical damage, should be constructed or protected and/or positioned to avoid danger.
- All electrical wiring that could result in personal danger must be either insulated, otherwise protected or positioned out of harm's way.
- A suitable means must be provided for:
  - cutting off the supply to any item of electrical equipment
  - enabling it to be securely isolated
  - identifying all electrical circuits.

Everyone who potentially will come into contact with live electrical wiring or equipment must be fully trained and competent in how to protect themselves and others.

3.4 Site electrical supply

The supply of electricity on construction sites will normally be provided by the public supply from the local electricity company, and/or the site generator, as a standby supply, if the public supply fails or where connection to the public supply is not practicable or is uneconomic.

3.4.1 Public supply

A public supply of electricity being provided depends on the following.

- Written application being made to the local electricity company, as soon as possible during the planning stage.
- Name, address, and telephone number of the contractor, or principal contractor where appointed, and developer, giving the full site address and a location plan.
- Details of the maximum demand load (in kilowatts) that is likely to be required during construction.
- Details of the maximum final demand load (in kilowatts) that will be required when the job is complete.
- Dates when the supply is needed.
- Discussion with electricity company staff to determine the necessary precautions to avoid damage or hazards from any existing overhead or underground cables.
- Establishment of supply points (where incoming cables will terminate), switch gear, metering equipment and requirements for earthing.

3.4.2 Generators

Generators may be required, even if for standby purposes, and will be powered by petrol or diesel engines. Attention should be given to the siting of such equipment in order to minimise pollution caused by noise and fumes. Other environmental considerations (such as fuel spillage and leaks) must also be considered (drip trays and bunds).

Site generators range from relatively small portable machines used to power one or two electrical tools to large, permanently sited standby machines capable of powering an extensive distribution system should the public system fail. It should be noted that some of the smaller machines have dual outputs (230/240 volt and 110 volt) meaning that making separate arrangements for deriving a 110 volt supply is not necessary. Generally, the output of the larger machines is a 415 volt, three-phase supply, mimicking the public supply arrangements.

It is normal for standby generating systems to auto-start upon the failure of the public supply. Such an unexpected event could have safety implications if the siting of a standby generator is not given due consideration.

Any permanently sited generating system, including the earthing arrangements, must be designed and installed by competent persons.

3.4.3 Calculating power requirements

The calculation for power requirements should be left to an experienced person or to the electricity supply company.

To enable the total site requirements to be established, an electrical demand table, which itemises all anticipated electrical loads, must be compiled. It is likely that a member of the site management team will become involved in this by advising upon the electrical loads that will be in use.

The person compiling the demand table will allow a diversity factor that acknowledges that not all electrical equipment will be in use at the same time.

3.5 Site distribution systems

With regard to new build, the term *site distribution system* refers to a temporary and flexible electrical distribution system that enables electrical power to be available around the site for construction purposes. However, with regard to refurbishment work or similar, the distribution system may comprise a combination of the fixed electrical system within the building (providing it is safe to leave it live) and elements of a temporary distribution system to enable hand tools, task lighting, and so on to be used.

3.5.1 Safe voltages

Mains voltage (230/240 volts) can be a killer. Apart from where absolutely necessary, 110 volt or battery-powered equipment must be used.

Generally, the site distribution system comprises of a combination of mains (230/240 volts or 415 volts) and low voltage (110 volt) circuits. To ensure that the appropriate supplies are available where they are required, and that there is no overloading of any part of the system, it must be designed and installed by competent persons.

Whilst it is likely that the main incoming supply will be at 230/240 volts or 415 volts, by using a transformer, the voltage present at the workface for hand tools, task lighting, and so on, should be reduced to a maximum of 110 volts. In some high risk situations, transformers are available to provide extra low voltages of 25 or 50 volts.

The way in which 110 volt systems are earthed means that the maximum voltage shock that anyone can receive is 55 volts, which is regarded as relatively safe for healthy adults. However, this voltage can still produce a current to flow, which can block the electrical signals between the brain and the muscles. This can stop the heart from beating properly, prevent the person from breathing or cause muscle spasms. Factors that will affect this are the size of the voltage, the parts of the body involved, how damp the person is and the length of time that the current is flowing.

3.5.2 Distribution equipment

Electrical distribution equipment must be obtained from a reputable supplier or hire company, to ensure that it has been manufactured to a known standard and tested. This is particularly important where electrical distribution equipment is to be sited outdoors, where the ingress of water and, to a lesser extent, dust could be a problem.

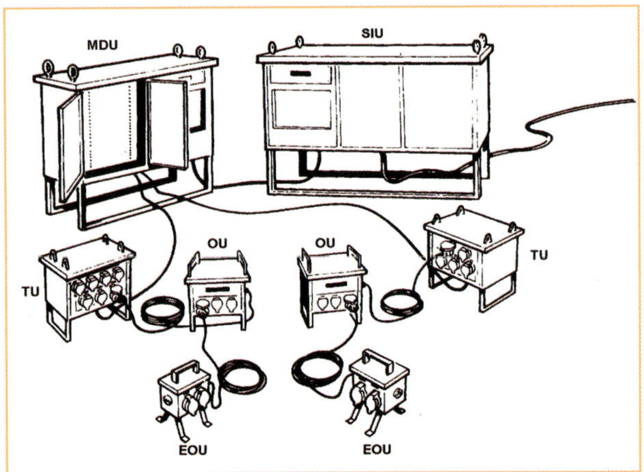

Different types of distribution equipment

There are many types of distribution equipment available, all of which are suitable for different situations.

- **Supply incoming units (SIU)** generally have a rating of up to 300 amps per phase. These units include main switch gear and metering equipment.
- **Mains distribution unit (MDU)** for the control and distribution of electricity on site, either 415 volts three-phase, or 230/240 volts single-phase AC.
- **Transformer units (TU)** are either single-phase (reducing 230/240 volts to 110 volts) or three-phase (reducing 415 volts to 110 volts). Such transformer units can be used for portable tools and plant, and general floor lighting.
- **Outlet units (OU)** 110 volt socket outlet units rated at 16 or 32 amp. Such outlet units can be used for portable tools, floodlighting and extension outlets. They are not usually protected by circuit-breakers.
- **Extension outlet units (EOU)** equipped with one or more 110 volt socket outlet, rated at 16 amp. Such units can be used for portable tools, local lighting and hand lamps. They are not usually protected by circuit-breakers.

In most cases at least part of each piece of distribution equipment will be colour coded to indicate its output voltage. Furthermore, the arrangement and number of pins within the electrical connecters are different for each voltage, which prevents, for example, a 110 volt power tool being plugged into a 230/240 volt supply unit.

The colour coding for distribution equipment is shown below.

(violet)	Violet	25 volts
(white)	White	50 volts
(yellow)	Yellow	110–130 volts

(blue)	Blue	220–240 volts
(red)	Red	380–415 volts
(black)	Black	500–650 volts

Case study example

On these projects the site team planned ahead and installed temporary supplies and general lighting to the soffit of main access routes. The lights in the foreground were fixed drops, each with two 110 volt sockets for equipment, which could be moved into rooms as and when required.

3.5.3 Residual current devices

All attempts should be made to use 110 volts or battery-powered tools where possible. However, it is inevitable that some 230/240 volt equipment will be in use, even if only in the site office. In such circumstances, the 230/240 volt supply must be supplied through an RCD. Another common situation in which a 230/240 volt supply is used is where work is carried out within an existing building in which the 230/240 volt circuits are still live, using a 110 volt hand tool and a 230/240 volt/110 volt transformer is the preferred option.

Under fault conditions, RCDs detect an imbalance in the current in the circuit and disconnect the supply before the person at risk can receive a potentially fatal electric shock.

There are two types of RCD.

- Those that are fitted as part of an electrical distribution system and, for example, are found within the supply panel for a site office (this type of RCD can only be installed by a competent electrician). The user should check these daily at the start of every shift, with a more formal visual inspection every week, and a combined inspection and test before the first use and then every three months.
- Plug-in RCDs (commonly known as power-breakers) that are plugged into a mains supply socket and have an in-built socket into which an individual mains-powered electrical tool or other appliance is plugged. The user should check these daily at the start of every shift, with a more formal visual inspection every week, and a combined inspection and test before the first use and then every month.

***Maintaining portable electrical equipment* (HSG107) suggests that portable residual current devices (RCDs) used on construction sites should have a combined inspection and test before first use.**

Both types of RCD have a test button that simulates a fault and operates the device.

- RCDs built into supply panels should be tested weekly.
- Power-breaker type devices should be tested before each use.

The following points should be noted

- RCDs do not reduce current flow or the voltage, only the time that the current flows (about 30 milliseconds), and thereby the severity of the shock.
- RCDs are delicate devices and should be treated with care. Advice on suitable RCDs for construction sites should be sought from manufacturers or suppliers.
- The use of an RCD does not give a 100% guarantee of safety.
- The device does not have a fail-safe feature and will not give an indication if it is faulty.

3.5.4 Site accommodation

The incoming electrical supply to site accommodation must be properly designed and be installed and commissioned by competent electrical contractors.

Site offices and welfare facilities are the only locations where electrical equipment that runs off a 230/240 volt supply should be in use. The electrical supply panel for such facilities must incorporate an RCD in each circuit. The correct operation of each RCD must be confirmed weekly by operating the test button, which should trip the device and switch off the circuit running through it.

All portable electrical equipment must be electrical safety tested (PAT) at appropriate intervals as decided by a competent person. This includes:

- common types of office equipment (such as fax machines and photocopiers)
- kitchen-type equipment (such as kettles, microwave ovens, and so on)
- small items (such as chargers for site radios and battery-powered tools).

For further information refer to the HSE publication *Maintaining portable electrical equipment* (HSG107).

3.6 Safe working practices with electricity

A number of people are killed and injured each year through accidents where the presence of electricity was a contributory factor. These accidents occur equally to electricians and to members of other trades. Some examples of why these accidents occur are shown below.

- The risks of doing the job had not been adequately assessed.
- Shortcuts in working practices were being taken.
- Pre-work investigation had failed to identify live electrical circuits (particularly in renovation projects).
- Circuits that had been made dead were re-energised by someone who did not realise that the system was being worked on by others.

For further detail refer to the HSE publications *Electrical safety and you: a brief guide* (INDG231) and *Electricity at work: safe working practices* (HSG85).

3.6.1 Assessing the risks

Working near to live electrical circuits and equipment can only be carried out safely once the significant risks of injury or death have been identified and effective control measures put in place to eliminate the risks or reduce them to an acceptable level. The people doing the work and anyone else who might be adversely affected by it must be informed of the significant risks arising out of the work and the part they must play in ensuring the work can be carried out safely.

The biggest risks arise out of deliberately working on live circuits or equipment and being unaware that nearby electrical equipment or wiring existed and/or was live.

The person carrying out the risk assessment, and reviewing and updating it at a later stage, must be sufficiently competent to identify the significant risks and to devise effective control measures.

3.6.2 Managing the risk during refurbishment work

Refurbishment projects pose particular electrical risks if the whole electrical system to the building is not made dead. A number of electrocutions have involved workers who were not electricians but who were carrying out other works (such as plumbers and joiners). These incidents could have been reduced or eliminated by the following.

- **Understanding the system.** Those responsible for planning and managing refurbishment work must understand the electrical system of the building in which the work takes place and liaise with the building occupier. This will enable building work to be planned and managed so that the integrity of the electrical system is not compromised and the workforce remains safe.
- **Working dead.** Relevant parts of the electrical system should be isolated if the refurbishment work (such as labouring, joinery or plumbing) is liable to disturb or damage the existing electrical system and expose people to electrical danger.
- **Portable electrical equipment.** Tools, plugs and cables designed for DIY and domestic use are not suitable for site conditions. You should use cordless tools or those that operate from a 110 volt supply system, earthed so that the maximum voltage does not exceed 55 volts. Regularly inspect power tools and take them out of service if they are damaged. Tools should be serviced by qualified electricians. Do not carry out makeshift repairs.
- **Residual current (trip) devices.** Where mains voltage (230/240 volts) is used, the risk of injury is high if equipment, tools or leads are damaged or there is a fault. Residual current or trip devices (RCDs) can ensure that the current is cut off promptly and safely if the equipment makes contact with any live part.
- **Lighting systems.** These protect cabling and bulbs against breakage. If a bulb breaks, the exposed filament may present a hazard. Have a system for checking bulbs regularly to maintain electrical safety and to keep the site well lit.

3.6.3 Effective isolation of circuits

3.6.3.1 Making sure the power is off

If a worker is working next to electrical circuits and they are not competent to check if the power is off, they must ask a competent person to do it for them, and watch them doing it. If they have any doubts about the method used, they should double-check with someone they know to be competent.

When checking that the power is off the competent person should be **sure** of the following.

- ☑ Device being used is suitable for the purpose of isolation.
- ☑ Isolator being used to turn off the power is working correctly and reliably.
- ☑ Switch being used is the only way that the circuit can be fed with electrical power.
- ☑ Switch being used is locked in the off position and cannot easily be turned on again.
- ☑ Equipment and method being used to check for voltage are in working order and are reliable.
- ☑ Isolation has been successful by confirming the circuit is no longer live.

Some electrical systems and equipment must be earthed before it is safe to work near them. Check whether this is necessary, and, if it is, ensure that this is done properly.

www.

For further information refer to the best practice guide (No. 2, Issue 2) from the Electrical Safety Council *Guidance on the management of electrical safety and safe isolation procedures for low-voltage installations.*

3.6.3.2 Making sure the power stays off (secure isolation)

If the electrical power has been turned off to allow work to be carried out safely, it is essential that the power stays off until the work is finished.

The person doing the work must make sure that **they** are in control and **stay** in control throughout the job. A good way is to have the only key to the switch or a locked room or cabinet containing the switch. Removing a fuse may seem to be a safe way of isolating a circuit but someone else could insert another one. Displaying notices could be equally or more ineffective as people often ignore them. If the person doing the job has any doubts that the electricity may be turned on again without them agreeing, they must know that they have the authority to stop work without delay and without having to check with a supervisor first.

Inadequate isolation

An electrician received a severe electric shock whilst carrying out building refurbishment and fitting out work in a new estates office. The electrical supply had not been properly isolated and an investigation revealed there was no management system in place to check precautions for electrical work.

The company was fined and prosecuted under the Health and Safety at Work Act, Section 2(1) and the Electricity at Work Regulations, Regulation 14.

Remember: it is the responsibility of those in control of work activities to direct those activities to reduce risks, so far as is practicable. This requires work to be properly planned and for safety precautions to be taken. Electricity supplies should be dead, and proved to be dead, before work commences, and the method of isolation should prevent inadvertent or deliberate re-energisation of the electrical system.

3.6.4 Locating hidden electrical wiring

The presence of electrical wires may not be obvious at the location where work is to be carried out but, as others have found out in the past, that does not mean that there are not any there. Even if some wiring is visible, there may be others that are buried within or hidden by the fabric of the building. Electrical wiring may sometimes look like pipes, and may be a range of colours.

Before anyone is allowed to start drilling or cutting into surfaces the person in charge of the job must complete the following.

- Look for the presence of electrical wires and any other hazards (such as asbestos). Remember to look on both sides of walls.
- Inspect plans of the electrical installation, and use these to find electrical wiring.
- Use a suitable cable detector if competent, or get a competent person to do it. Remember that some cable detectors will not find a wire carrying a small or no current – consult the user guide.
- Identify nearby electrical equipment or installations and try to establish from which direction the wiring runs to these.
- Identify and provide equipment that will minimise the risks during the work.
- Ensure that suitable personal protective equipment (PPE) is identified and used.
- Make it clear to the person doing the job that they must **stop work** and check with their supervisor if they have any doubts as to the safety of what they are about to do.

3.6.5 Permit to work

Permit to work systems are essential to ensure safe working where live electrical supplies, cables and equipment exist, particularly in installation, maintenance or construction work.

The Electricity at Work Regulations requires employers to implement safe systems of work in circumstances where a person could be exposed to live conductors or equipment. A permit to work system must be a part of that safe system. In the case of construction sites, permits to work are more commonly used whilst the site electrical distribution system is itself being worked on, or connections made to it, thereby potentially exposing live parts.

Tight control of the permit system is essential if its integrity is to be maintained. A competent and authorised person, often the electrical contractor's site manager, must be appointed to raise and co-ordinate the issue of permits. Other people who will be involved in completing parts of the permit and signing accordingly are anyone who has been involved in making the work area and system to be worked on safe, and the person directly in charge of the workers doing the work.

Companies will design their own permits to suit their needs, but for an example of a typical permit refer to Section G: *Checklists and forms*.

Some companies use permits printed on carbonised paper, which provide identical second or even third copies, where the company's record keeping system demands them.

Most permits contain provisions for the physical locking off of switches, and the retention or display of keys or permits.

One copy of the permit must be retained for the duration of the work by the person to whom it is issued. Before apparatus is made live again, the permit must be returned for cancellation. At cancellation, it must be countersigned by both the holder and the authorised person.

The authorised person should keep a record in the job file of the issued permits and their cancellation.

Before work starts, the authorised person should ensure that the permit to work will cover the making safe of the part of the system to be worked on, from all possible sources of supply.

If the work is handed over from one competent person to another, the permit is to be endorsed by the authorised person and transferred to the second operative.

Under no circumstances should anyone work on, maintain, repair or otherwise adjust high-voltage apparatus, except in accordance with the instructions and terms of a formal permit to work.

3.6.6 Monitoring contractors

In addition to electrical contractors, many other trades (examples of which are shown below) will have an electrical element to their work.

- Heating and ventilation engineers.
- Lift and escalator engineers.
- Plumbers.
- Fire detection and control engineers.
- Security and CCTV engineers.

The work of such contractors and others installing electrical circuits, or simply connecting to electrical equipment installed by others, must be carefully monitored to ensure that they do not jeopardise electrical safety or leave an installation in a dangerous condition.

The **person in charge** of the site, or someone else appointed to do so, must complete the following.

- Inspect the risk assessments of these contractors to establish if their work could possibly adversely affect the safety of others working nearby, or who might otherwise be affected by their work.
- Inspect any written scheme of work (method statement) to establish if any element will conflict with other works.
- Periodically liaise with the contractors to establish if the risk assessment should be reviewed and updated.
- Co-ordinate work as necessary to make sure that no-one is put at risk unnecessarily.
- Ensure that higher risk work is carried out in accordance with a permit to work system.
- Monitor the work of the contractors on a periodic basis to make sure it is carried out in accordance with the method statement and any permits.
- Make sure that the equipment used by the contractors is suitable for the job in hand, particularly in higher risk situations (such as working in cramped conditions where there is a lot of earthed metalwork or in a damp or wet environment, for example inside a tank).
- Make sure that the contractors implement a strict locking-off procedure where there is potential for them or others to come into contact with live parts due to circuits being made live again whilst work is still being carried out.
- Where necessary ensure that appropriate signage is displayed, but also appreciate that signage in itself is not an adequate safety measure.
- Ensure that contractors do not allow their combustible waste materials to accumulate in areas where it could become the fuel in the event of an electrical fire.

Particular care is needed in respect of any alterations and extensions to existing installations (for example, in renovation work), particularly in the identification of circuits where some circuits could remain live for at least part of the work.

With regard to **electrical contractors** working on site, as far as is practical, the site management team must assure themselves of the following.

- The contractor has compiled an accurate assessment of the risks to their employees and other people who may be affected by the work.
- The people at risk are aware and know what to do to protect themselves.
- An objective decision has been taken over whether the job can be carried out with the circuit(s) live or dead.
- The work will be properly planned, which includes the contractor informing site management of the circuit(s) to be worked on, and the implications for others (for example, if they have to disable a fire detection system).
- The job will be adequately supervised, with permanent accompaniment where necessary (see paragraph below).
- The contractors will implement a permit to work system where justified by the risks.
- A written system of working (method statement) will be produced, communicated to those doing the job, and followed.
- The contractor will provide briefings to their employees and to others, as necessary.
- The contractor has employed only competent employees.
- The contractor will provide the correct tools and test equipment.
- The contractor's employees will be provided with suitable and sufficient PPE.

Where it is necessary to work on **live equipment**, it will usually be necessary for the person doing the work to be accompanied by another person. It is essential that this person:

- can recognise the signs of danger
- is able to administer first aid for electric shock
- can otherwise give assistance in the event of an emergency
- knows how to switch off the supply
- can assist in restricting access to the area.

Where practicable, only use hand-held power tools a minimum of 500 mm away from the indicated line of a service, buried in or below a hard surface.

For further information on working near to underground and overhead services refer to Chapter D08.

04 Temporary works

Contents

Overview

The requirement to manage temporary works can be misunderstood and many believe it is only required on large projects or for complex work. However, temporary works are likely to form a vital part of any construction project.

The Health and Safety Executive (HSE) report *Preventing catastrophic events in construction* identified that insufficient consideration is given to the management of temporary works. This leaves projects open to risks, such as injuries or fatalities, the failure or collapse of both temporary and permanent works, damage to adjacent premises, and the consequent delays and increased costs.

Temporary works, design, planning, execution and interfaces with plant and equipment must all be taken seriously.

This chapter aims to raise awareness of temporary works and the legal requirements to manage them.

4.1 Introduction

An important element of all construction projects relates to those items used to assist in the construction, but which do not usually form part of the final (permanent) works.

These are wide ranging but some examples are shown below.

- Site hoardings and signboards.
- Temporary access roadways and working platforms for plant.
- Temporary earthworks.
- Scaffolding and other proprietary systems used for access or support.
- Excavations and excavation supports.
- Propping systems.
- Formwork.

Although, on completion, it is the permanent works that receive attention, without temporary works being properly thought out and managed, the project will not be successful.

Effective, safe and perhaps imaginatively designed temporary works solutions can bring significant benefit and improve projects in terms of safety, certainty, productivity, efficiency, quality, completion times and cost.

On the other hand, poorly planned, designed, constructed, supervised and managed temporary works leave projects open to risks (such as injuries or fatalities, the failure or collapse of both temporary and permanent works, damage to adjacent premises, and the consequent delays and increased costs).

Two other terms are related to temporary works are given below.

- **Falsework**, which is the temporary support given to structures until they are able to sustain their own loads.
- **Formwork**, which is the temporary form/mould (usually steel or timber) used to contain concrete until it has attained sufficient strength to withstand its own weight.

Temporary works are important for several reasons.

- Often they form a significant part of the overall cost of the project.
- They have the potential to cause delay and additional cost if not thought through in adequate detail.
- They are often safety-critical (for example, if they fail, there is a high probability that someone will be hurt or killed).
- Often they have important characteristics that do not apply to permanent works *(refer to 4.2)*.

As for all aspects of construction projects it is important that, at all stages:

- it is clear who is responsible for what
- all relevant parties on site are aware of this demarcation
- all parties have adequate competence, resource and information to fulfil their role.

This is particularly critical at interfaces, such as between temporary works and permanent works, between different elements of temporary works or where there are abnormal loads in the permanent works during construction.

e.g. Tower crane

Consider the following situation. The permanent works foundation is to be used as a base for a tower crane. Some modifications of this foundation are required to accommodate the tower crane fixings.

Element	Designation	Comment
Foundation	Permanent works	Used as temporary works to found tower crane (with permanent works designer approval).
Foundation adaptation	Temporary works	Included to facilitate fixings; will become permanent works if it is not removed on completion (with permanent works designer approval).
Fixings into base	Temporary works	Co-ordinated with foundation layout and reinforcement details. Requires design check and co-ordination with permanent works designer.
Tower crane	Plant	Removed on completion.

The elements described above will involve several parties: permanent works designer, temporary works designer, contractor (foundation), supplier (fixings), supplier (crane). Unless the design and construction interfaces between these organisations and activities are adequately managed, and considered in advance of the work, delay or failure could result.

4.2 Characteristics of temporary works

Temporary works often have characteristics that are not present in permanent works or which present themselves differently (see table below).

Construction accuracy	Although some temporary works have specified/recommended accuracy (specifically in respect of how upright they should be), some do not. Experience shows that, generally, accuracy is less likely to be achieved with temporary works than with permanent works. However, it can be important in order to achieve the assumed strength and robustness.
Misalignment of components	Assemblies made up of small components (such as proprietary falsework towers) may incorporate misalignments between sections.
Reuse	Unlike the permanent works, temporary works components are reused and hence the risk of damage, fatigue cracking or distortion should be recognised and managed.
Changes	Unauthorised changes (for example, in the layout or by removal of components that obstruct trades) can seriously compromise the safety of temporary works.
Abuse	Temporary works can be prone to abuse in the form of overloading, impact and poor quality control (such as welding), unless adequately managed.
Utilisation	As temporary works are designed for a specific task they are usually loaded to their full design load. Permanent works are rarely loaded to this extent.

Site management procedures should recognise these characteristics to ensure that none occur to an extent detrimental to the effective use or safety of the temporary works being used.

4.3 Responsibilities

Responsibilities for temporary works arise in two ways: through the contract and via the statutory law.

4.3.1 Contract

Although the contractor will have the overall responsibility for temporary works, it is important that all sub-contracts are clear as to what obligations are passed on to others and how sub-contractors are to interact with other sub-contractors and the main contractor. Contracts should require the use of good practice approaches (such as British Standards, industry guides, and so on). *(For good practice on avoiding ambiguity and disputes, and to ensure high standards are attained, refer to 4.5.)*

Site managers will play an important role by ensuring this interaction occurs in a timely manner, that decisions are recorded and that designers (of permanent or temporary works) are consulted when appropriate. Although most of this action will be undertaken by the temporary works co-ordinator (TWC) it is important that the site manager maintains an overview and that the interface between site manager and TWC is set out in the company procedures.

4.3.2 Statute

Statutory requirements are legally binding and they override any contractual stipulations. There is no differentiation between temporary works and permanent works under the law: any hazardous work must be managed safely. The main requirements, which stem from the Construction (Design and Management) Regulations (CDM), are set out, in summary, in the table below.

<table>
<tr><td>Co-ordination, co-operation and communication</td><td>All parties are obligated to co-ordinate, co-operate and communicate to ensure that temporary works are safe, and will not cause unnecessary ill effects upon the health of those involved.</td></tr>
<tr><td colspan="2">This requirement is common sense. It will not only help to avoid accidents and ill health but also is an essential ingredient for a successful project. Contract requirements need to set out how this can be achieved (such as site meetings and information flow mechanisms). Risk thrives at interfaces.</td></tr>
<tr><td>Competency</td><td>It is obligatory on all parties to be satisfied that they have the skills, knowledge and training to carry out the tasks assigned to them, and for the engaging party to be equally satisfied.</td></tr>
<tr><td colspan="2">The employment of a sub-contractor or designer who is not capable of safe or efficient working, or lacks experience, will sooner or later create a liability. It is important to have control over any further sub-contracting by sub-contractors themselves.</td></tr>
<tr><td>Timing</td><td>All parties must be afforded sufficient time to plan, mobilise and execute the works. This includes those involved in the design or execution of temporary works. Hence good project planning is essential.</td></tr>
<tr><td colspan="2">To facilitate this early consideration to the brief, information, constraints, sequencing, and so on, will pay dividends.</td></tr>
<tr><td>Pre-construction data</td><td>Under the CDM Regulations the principal contractor or contractor will have received data from the client or design team; some of this may be relevant to temporary works design or execution. If so it is important that it is passed to those sub-contractors or designers who are involved.</td></tr>
<tr><td colspan="2">One of the recurrent complaints from sub-contractors is that they do not receive such data.</td></tr>
<tr><td>Construction phase plan</td><td>This is the document that records the health and safety management arrangements relating to, amongst other things, temporary works.</td></tr>
<tr><td colspan="2">Those elements of the plan that may be relevant to others must be passed to them by the principal contractor or contractor.</td></tr>
<tr><td>Inspections</td><td>Some temporary works (such as scaffolding and falsework, cofferdams and excavations) are required to have statutory inspections before use, after amendments or any significant adverse event.</td></tr>
</table>

Other regulations will also apply, as appropriate, (such as the Provision and Use of Work Equipment Regulations (PUWER), the Lifting Operations and Lifting Equipment Regulations (LOLER) and the Work at Height Regulations. All of these have inspection requirements.

4.4 Hazards arising from temporary works

Temporary works do not produce hazards that differ significantly from the permanent works.

Generic hazards for safety and health are shown below.

- Safety.
  - Structural adequacy.
  - Work at height.
  - Falling objects.
  - Operational management.
- Health.
  - Manual handling.
  - Operational management.

Other hazards will apply on specific projects.

Operational management failure (safety)

A façade scaffold collapsed in Milton Keynes causing the death of a worker and injuring several others, because of poor operational site management.

Poor management of temporary works resulting in a scaffolding collapse

Specifically:

- ☑ failure to inspect the scaffold on a regular basis
- ☑ unauthorised changes
- ☑ overloading
- ☑ insufficient ties.

Each of these issues may have been considered small in themselves, but cumulatively, and over time, they caused a tragic failure.

4.5 Good practice

Good practice, drawn up by industry itself, will help not only in the management of a safe site, but also in creating a productive site. Good practice may be divided into **management** and **technical**.

4.5.1 Management

The accepted core document, in place for more than 30 years, is BS 5975: *Code of Practice for temporary works procedures and the permissible stress design of falsework*. This code should be embedded in all contracts to avoid any dispute or uncertainty as to the expected procedures. The main items are shown below.

Designated individual	There should be one person in each organisation who establishes and implements the procedures (temporary works design and construction), including the appointment of competent TWCs. Site managers should be familiar with these procedures.
Temporary works co-ordinators (TWC)	On each contract the contractor or principal contractor should appoint one of its own personnel to act as TWC. It is important that the duties are in writing and made known. The TWC is responsible for ensuring that all aspects of the organisation's procedures relating to the co-ordination and management of temporary works are implemented on site. A schedule of TWC duties is provided in BS 5975 (Clause 7.2.5). It is preferable that the TWC is not the person responsible for day-to-day progress of the temporary works on site. Where this is unavoidable, the TWC should ensure that decisions relating to temporary works are safety-based and not influenced by other commercial concerns.
Temporary works supervisors (TWS)	On larger or more complex projects it may be desirable for the appointment, from sub-contractors, of one or more TWS to assist the TWC. It is important that the duties are in writing and made known.
Temporary works register	All sites should have a register of the temporary works giving: ▪ a brief description ▪ which parties are designing and executing the work ▪ significant dates. The first entry is likely to be site hoarding.
Permits to load/unload	No temporary works should be loaded or unloaded without the authorisation of the TWC.
Information flow	The code stresses the importance of good information flow and co-ordination. Specifically, designers should always have a written brief.

There are occasions when choosing a solution with greater initial cost may have overall benefits that outweigh this expense. Some examples are shown below.

- ☑ Use of prefabricated staircase assemblies to gain vertical access, in lieu of ladders. Staircases allow quick access, multiple usage, and the carrying of tools.
- ☑ Use of proprietary barrier systems allows quick installation.
- ☑ Formwork with integrated working platforms allows instant, safe and effective access.

4.5.2 Technical

BS 5975 also contains rules for design. Falsework should be designed to these rules or to the European Standards (for example, BS EN 12812) by competent persons with experience in falsework design. Detailed advice is outside the scope of this chapter.

All temporary works should be constructed from drawings and sketches authorised for use by the TWC. Some important watch-points, not requiring explicit technical expertise, are shown below.

- ☑ Adequate foundations to falsework (if it doesn't look right, it probably isn't).
- ☑ Lateral bracing at forkhead level (although some systems and arrangements do not need bracing it is better to check if none are present).
- ☑ All scaffolding requires a formal engineered design, unless it is a basic scaffold, as defined in TG20.
- ☑ General standard of construction (such as verticality, alignment).
- ☑ Adequate protection to those working in excavations.

4.6 Use of equipment and materials

Temporary works uniquely utilises materials that may have been used previously. It should:

- ☑ come from a reputable source
- ☑ be authenticated, when relevant
- ☑ come with guidance if its safe use is dependent upon the manner in which it is used
- ☑ be inspected (usually prior to delivery) for condition, cracks and distortion, depending upon the component.

The contractor ordering this equipment should have procedures in place to ensure these points are recognised and actioned.

It is particularly important, when using proprietary equipment, to be satisfied that the component is the genuine article.

4.7 What can go wrong?

Most temporary works, following statutory requirements and good practice, are executed without any problem. Nonetheless, there are numerous examples of failure where significant cost, delay and human suffering have resulted.

The most common category of failing is lack of management. This is shown in the table below.

Aspect	Example
General	Insufficient oversight by the contractor or principal contractor (which will have responsibilities notwithstanding any contractual sub-letting). Failure to appoint a TWC or to provide adequate technical back-up.
Change control	Unauthorised changes (such as removal of members to allow access for another trade).
Loading	Stacking of materials on working platforms that are only designed for access or light loads.
Time	Insufficient time allowed for elements of the supply chain to undertake their task. This often happens at sub-sub-contract level.
Information	Poor appreciation by the instructing party of the information required by designers and others to deliver a compliant (and safe) output.
Lateral support	Insufficient ties into adjacent structures to provide the necessary lateral support.
Sheeting	Sheeting scaffolds and other above-ground structures (for protection or advertising), which have not been designed for such action.

4.8 Briefing and receiving data

4.8.1 Briefing

It is important that those being employed as temporary works contractors or designers are fully briefed. Notwithstanding the requirements of CDM, BS 5975 sets out requirements (Section 8), as does BE EN 12812 (Section 6) but only for design class B2. It is important to check that these clauses are sufficient for the particular needs and to appreciate that they do not always apply.

Advice should be sought where the temporary works are beyond the experience of site management.

4.8.2 Receiving data

Equally important is that those employed to design or construct temporary works provide information on any limitations or requirements relating to their work that might impact on others. Notwithstanding the requirements of CDM, BS 5975 sets out requirements (Section 9), as does BS EN 12812 (Section 9) providing a list of required data but only for Classes B1 and B2. As above it is necessary to be satisfied that this is sufficient for the specific case.

Examples of the important data required are shown below.

- ✓ Lateral stability assumptions (such as vertical assemblies relying on the permanent works).
- ✓ Pour rate assumed (for vertical formwork).
- ✓ Whether the structure may be sheeted.
- ✓ Size of tie bolts assumed.
- ✓ (Batter) slope inclination for excavations.

4.9 Generic checklist

It is not possible to produce specific checklists, as temporary works come in a wide range of forms and all are influenced by site-specific situations. However, the following provide an overall reminder.

Is the proposal safety-critical (if it failed, could anyone be hurt or have their health affected)?

- ✓ If 'Yes', all organisations (and individuals) have statutory responsibilities. Clear procedures are essential.
- ✗ If 'No', a problem can nonetheless still cause delay or direct financial loss. Hence, it is a sensible contractual precaution to follow the same guideline principles.

Is there a TWC appointed, acting in accordance with BS 5975?

- ✓ If 'Yes', ensure the interface between the TWC and site management is clear and operational. If you are the TWC, ensure you know your obligations and whether you may need to seek assistance.
  - If you are also responsible for site management ensure you are able to exercise the TWC duties independently from other management pressures.
- ✗ If 'No', you should refer the matter to the designated individual. The designated individual is the person within the organisation with specific allocated responsibilities for the setting and implementation of temporary works procedures.

Some small sites can produce substantial risk (such as refurbishments involving structural alterations, basement constructions and deep excavations).

4.10 Supporting information

- ✓ *Code of Practice for temporary works procedures and the permissible stress design of falsework* (BS 5975:2008 plus Amendment A1 2011).
- ✓ *Guide to good practice for scaffolding with tubes and fittings* (NASC TG20.13).
- ✓ *Temporary works – Principles of design and construction* (Thomas Telford 2012).

For further information refer to the Temporary Works forum website.

C
04

05

Plant and work equipment

Contents

Supporting information

G: Checklists and forms

GT 700 Toolbox talks

Overview

Over the last five years an average of 46 people have been killed each year in the construction industry. A significant number of these fatalities were caused by plant and work equipment. The majority could have been avoided by effective planning and control of plant use, adequate checking, inspection and maintenance of the plant and equipment, and thorough training, assessment and briefing of personnel.

This chapter gives an overview of the legal requirements for plant and work equipment and the steps required to ensure that these obligations are met, so that work equipment can be used safely and efficiently.

5.1 Introduction

All plant and tools used on construction sites are defined as work equipment by the Provision and Use of Work Equipment Regulations (PUWER), and have the potential to cause harm. Reducing the risk of harm caused by work equipment requires the following steps.

- Assessment of the hazards and risks involved in using work equipment.
- Implementation of measures to eliminate or reduce those risks.
- Ensuring that operators of work equipment are trained and competent.
- Ensuring that work equipment is checked, maintained and inspected.

Problems with plant and work equipment operations often occur because of poor communication, both during planning and briefing of operators and users of work equipment.

5.2 Important points

- The term *work equipment* is very wide ranging and refers to any item of equipment, machinery or tools being used to carry out work.
- The word *used* means any activity involving the work equipment, including starting, stopping, repairing, modifying, maintaining, servicing or cleaning.
- Examples of work equipment are an excavator, a crane, a hammer, an angle grinder and a cartridge tool.
- All items of work equipment must comply with certain legal requirements.
- Broadly speaking, the effort necessary to comply with the requirements will depend upon the complexity of the equipment and its potential to cause harm (for example, a trowel will not require the same level of inspection as a passenger goods hoist).
- The law also requires anyone who uses an item of work equipment to be trained and competent to do so.
- The effort and time needed to achieve the required level of competence will depend upon the complexity of the equipment and its potential to cause harm.
- Work equipment must be maintained and inspected as necessary to ensure that it can continue to be used safely.
- Certain work equipment must also be subjected to thorough examination.

5.3 Legislative requirements

The following is a brief summary of the legislative requirements for mobile plant operations.

5.3.1 Provision and Use of Work Equipment Regulations

The PUWER are concerned with such matters as suitability for purpose of work equipment, safeguarding of dangerous parts of machinery, provision of appropriate controls, training of operators and maintenance of work equipment, including cranes and lifting equipment.

PUWER places duties on any person who has control to any extent of any of the following.

- Work equipment.
- A person at work who uses, supervises or manages the use of work equipment.
- The way in which work equipment is used at work (including maintenance).

PUWER applies to employers in respect of work equipment provided for, or used by, their employees, self-employed persons and other persons (such as visitors).

5.3.2 Lifting Operations and Lifting Equipment Regulations

The Lifting Operations and Lifting Equipment Regulations (LOLER) deal with the specific risks arising from the use of work equipment (including lifting accessories) to lift loads. They build upon PUWER and apply to the same groups of people.

The requirements of LOLER are shown below.

- All lifting operations must be planned, supervised and carried out safely.
- Specific requirements must be applied to the lifting of people.
- Pre-use checks and inspections at appropriate intervals must be carried out on lifting equipment.
- Lifting equipment must be thoroughly examined by a competent person on specified occasions and at specified intervals.

5.3.3 Pressure Systems Safety Regulations

The Pressure Systems Safety Regulations deal with the specific risk arising from pressure systems, both fixed and portable. The regulations set out requirements for the following.

- Design and construction.
- Provision of information and marking.
- Installation.
- Use.
- Maintenance, modification and repair.
- Examination.

The Pressure Systems Safety Regulations apply to all portable fire extinguishers.

5.3.4 Work at Height Regulations

The Work at Height Regulations impose health and safety requirements for work at height. Some of these requirements are shown below.

- Organisation and planning, including rescue from height.
- Hierarchy of control.
- Competence and supervision.
- Steps to be taken to avoid risk from work at height.
- Selection of work equipment.
- Inspection of work equipment.

Work at height

The regulations define work at height as:

- work in any place, including a place at or below ground level
- obtaining access to or egress from such place while at work, except by a staircase in a permanent workplace, where, if measures required by these regulations were not taken, a person could fall a distance liable to cause personal injury.

5.3.5 Construction (Design and Management) Regulations

The CDM Regulations place duties on duty holders, including clients, designers and contractors, for the planning, management and monitoring of health, safety and welfare in construction projects and of the co-ordination of the performance of these duties by duty holders. These include a duty on every person working under the control of another to report anything that they are aware is likely to endanger health or safety.

Certain individual regulations have implications for the way in which plant and work equipment operations are carried out.

- There must be safe places of work, including getting to and from the place of work.
- Traffic routes must be suitable for the vehicles that will have to pass over them (for example, dumpers must be used and moved in a way that does not put pedestrians at risk).
- There must be suitable and sufficient lighting for every place of work and traffic route.

5.3.6 Personal Protective Equipment at Work Regulations

These regulations impose health and safety requirements for the provision of, and use by, persons at work of personal protective equipment (PPE). The following points are some of the requirements of the regulations.

- Employers ensure suitable PPE is provided, without charge, for their employees.
- Self-employed persons ensure suitable PPE is provided for them.
- Employers and self-employed persons meet specific requirements for the training, selection, use, storage and maintenance of PPE.
- Employees report to their employer the loss of, or any obvious defect in, PPE.

5.3.7 Control of Vibration at Work Regulations

These regulations require employers to assess the vibration risk to their employees and eliminate risk or reduce exposure. Some other employer requirements are listed below.

- ☑ Provide information to their employees.
- ☑ Keep records of risk assessments and control actions.
- ☑ Keep records of health surveillance.
- ☑ Regularly review and update risk assessments.

5.3.8 Control of Noise at Work Regulations

The Control of Noise at Work Regulations require employers to complete the following.

- ☑ Assess the risks to their employees from noise at work.
- ☑ Take action to reduce the noise exposure that produces those risks.
- ☑ Provide their employees with hearing protection if the noise cannot be reduced enough by using other methods.
- ☑ Make sure the legal limits on noise exposure are not exceeded.
- ☑ Provide their employees with information, instruction and training.
- ☑ Carry out health surveillance where there is a risk to health.

5.3.9 Control of Substances Hazardous to Health Regulations

The Control of Substances Hazardous to Health (COSHH) Regulations require employers to control substances that are hazardous to health by the following means.

- ☑ Finding out what the health hazards are.
- ☑ Deciding how to prevent harm to health (risk assessment).
- ☑ Providing control measures to reduce harm to health.
- ☑ Making sure control measures are used.
- ☑ Keeping all control measures in good working order.
- ☑ Providing information, instruction and training for employees and others.
- ☑ Providing monitoring and health surveillance in appropriate cases.
- ☑ Planning for emergencies.

5.3.10 Supply of Machinery (Safety) Regulations

The Supply of Machinery (Safety) Regulations are the UK's implementation of European Union Directive 2006/42/EC, the Machinery Directive, which requires that all machinery (including lifting accessories) supplied into the European Union, meets the essential health and safety requirements detailed in Schedule 2 of the regulations. Each machine must be accompanied at the time of supply by an EC declaration of conformity, declaring that the machinery fulfils all the relevant provisions of the regulations.

Plant, first supplied after 1 January 1995, must be CE marked and meet the essential health and safety requirements of the Supply of Machinery (Safety) Regulations. Consequently, most items of lifting equipment are designed to a harmonised European Standard (such as EN 474-5 for excavators, EN 1459 for telehandlers and EN 12001 for concrete pumps).

5.3.11 British, European and ISO standards

Standards do not generally have the force of law. The application of a standard is almost always voluntary, although standards are very often used in support of legislation, and compliance with a standard is sometimes quoted in legislation as offering a route to discharging legal obligations. A good example of this is the references to the BS 7121 series in the guidance to LOLER.

British standards are generally restricted to Codes of Practice (CoPs) for safe use of equipment (such as BS 7121-1:2006 *Safe use of cranes*), whilst European (EN) standards cover requirements for basic principles (Type A), common product requirements (Type B) and specific product requirements (Type C) (such as EN 474-6 *Earth-moving machinery. Safety – Requirements for dumpers)*.

International Standards (ISO) cover both the safe use and specification of lifting equipment. They do not have any legal status but are often taken as good practice and are cited as normative references in some EN product standards.

For more detailed information on legislation refer to Section A: *Legal and management*.

5.4 General work equipment

The building, construction and civil engineering industry uses a vast range of plant and equipment, all of which has to comply with PUWER. It is all referred to as work equipment and includes the following.

- Hand tools (such as hammers and screwdrivers).
- Powered tools, including electric and pneumatic (such as hand drills and circular saws).
- Lifting equipment and accessories (covered under PUWER as well as having requirements under LOLER).
- Testing and laboratory equipment (such as cube crushers).
- Complex structures and machines made up of other components and equipment (such as scaffolds).

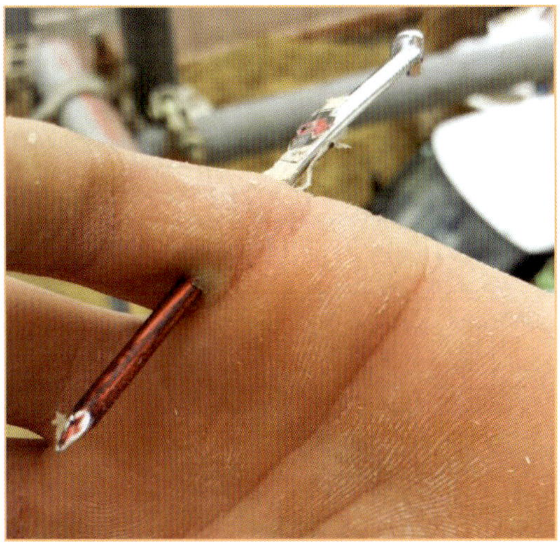

Poor practice and lack of concentration can lead to injuries

Some types of powered hand tools (such as engine-powered cutting-off machines and chainsaws) have the potential to cause severe personal injury unless they are used by trained and competent persons in appropriate circumstances.

Another type of equipment commonly used in the construction industry with the potential to cause harm, if not properly used, is mechanical equipment that operates through the application of leverage or torque. This include jacks, winches and various cutting and bending tools that incorporate manually operated mechanisms.

Tools and equipment operated by air may also cause significant injuries due to failure of the tools or the connections to the compressor.

All items of plant are classified as work equipment, including static and mobile equipment, pedestrian-controlled equipment, ride-on equipment and remote-controlled equipment. Plant used in construction operations on site includes static plant used in the actual construction work (such as mixers and pumps).

For further information refer to the HSE publication *Safe use of work equipment* (L22).

5.4.1 Suitability for purpose

All equipment that is used to carry out a work activity must be suitable for that work.

Improvisation is dangerous and can lead to serious accidents occurring. Both a hand-held circular saw being used instead of a router to cut grooves or rebates in timber, or a dumper being used to transport persons, have the potential to create dangerous situations.

All work equipment must be regularly maintained in an effective state, in an effective working order and in good repair. Work equipment that is covered by LOLER must be subjected to thorough examinations.

For further information refer to Chapter C07 Lifting operations.

5.4.2 Conformity with EU requirements

Employers should ensure that any work equipment that is in use or acquired, either new or second-hand, has a CE mark. This indicates that it complies with the relevant European Directive and has been manufactured to appropriate standards.

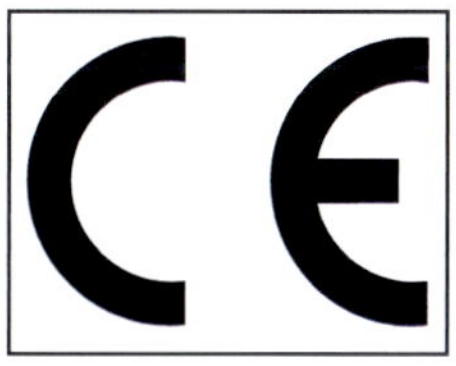

CE mark

5.4.3 'Grey' imports

Machines originally supplied from outside the EU frequently do not comply with the requirements of the Machinery Directive and are not CE marked. If such machines are brought into the EU they cannot be used until they have been modified to meet EU requirements. This is a time-consuming and costly process that often negates the benefit of purchasing second-hand machines from outside of the EU.

5.4.4 Mobile plant

This includes excavators, dumpers, forklifts, telehandlers, rollers, mobile elevating work platforms (MEWPs) and mobile cranes. Mobile plant may either be controlled by the operator riding on the machine or they may be pedestrian controlled.

For specific details on mobile plant refer to Chapter C06 Mobile plant and vehicles.

C
05

5.4.5 Static plant

This includes items such as construction hoists *(refer to Chapter C08 Lifting equipment),* compressors and pumps (*refer to 5.8 and 5.9*), batching plants, concrete mixers, and rebar benders and cutters.

5.4.6 Lifting equipment

Both mobile and static plant may be designed as lifting equipment for lifting operations. This includes mobile cranes, tower cranes, MEWPs, hoists, telehandlers and excavators used for lifting.

For further information refer to Chapter C07 Lifting operations and Chapter C08 Lifting equipment.

5.4.7 Manually operated hand-held plant and work equipment

In recent years, the mechanisation of techniques that were traditionally seen as being achievable only by using non-mechanical equipment has caused an upsurge in the range of equipment that is available.

Selection of the correct equipment for the job in hand is vitally important. Choosing modern equipment that reduces the risk of injury or ill health is fundamental to creating safer working environments.

The environment in which the equipment is used also has a bearing on the safety of the operative. In certain circumstances it **may** be safe to use hand tools in a confined space, but to use powered equivalents could have fatal results.

Hand-held power tools, whether powered electrically, by internal combustion engine, hydraulically, by cartridge or compressed air, are covered by the definition.

As the use of these types of tool has increased, so has the potential for serious injury. Old type, hand-operated smoothing planes could cause serious cuts if wrongly used, but those injuries bear no comparison with the injuries that could occur when wrongly using their modern electrically powered equivalent.

Cutting chases in a wall using an older type cutting disc produces unacceptable amounts of dust. Modern equipment that is fitted with a dust suppression mechanism is safer and much healthier.

Also included within this category is the type of equipment that requires human effort in its operation (such as jacks, bar-bending machines, pipe-threaders and other machines where the principles of leverage or torque are utilised).

Many jobs (such as nailing tiling battens on a roof), which traditionally would have been completed by using a hammer, are now carried out by nail guns powered by gas canisters. Equipment of this type is open to abuse, which can result in horrific consequences. It is possible to propel a nail in free flight from a nail gun, giving it the lethal potential of a firearm. (*For further information refer to 5.6 Portable fixing tools.*)

5.4.8 Hand tools

The general requirements of PUWER apply as much to hand tools as they do to more complex items of work equipment. Unfortunately, this is often not appreciated by hand tool users, who tend to only deal with problems when they occur, rather than eliminating hazards in the first place.

Two examples are shown below.

- Cold chisels with burred-over mushroom heads can result in a person losing an eye when a burr breaks off during use.
- A hammer head becoming detached from its shaft can cause a serious injury to the user or a person nearby.

In both examples, the potential to cause harm can be substantially reduced if a system of regular checks, inspection and maintenance, as required by the regulations, is instigated.

5.4.9 Non-mechanical access equipment

5.4.9.1 Scaffolds

If incorrectly erected or exposed to misuse, scaffolds can also be the cause of accidents. Therefore, such equipment must meet the following requirements.

- Be suitably designed.
- Comprise suitable components that have been inspected prior to use.
- Be regularly inspected every seven days or after alteration, damage or high winds, the results of the inspection recorded, and proactive maintenance regimes put into place.
- Not be interfered with or altered by untrained individuals.

Many accidents have occurred due to installation of scaffold with damaged equipment (such as split boards and bent tubes).

For further information on access scaffolding refer to Chapter D04 Scaffolding.

5.4.9.2 Ladders and other wooden access equipment

Work equipment made from wood will not last forever and will deteriorate with age and use. Regular inspection of the equipment is essential for safety, will prolong its useful life and give an early indication of deterioration. It is commonplace for inspections of ladders and steps to be formally recorded, with each ladder or step being given a specific identifying number.

The main issue with wooden ladders and steps is that they must not be painted or treated with anything that would hide any faults or defects.

The regular inspection of wooden builders' steps must include the hinges that connect the support stays and the restraining rope that controls the opening of the steps, as well as the condition of the timber.

Wooden extension ladders have ropes, pulley blocks and clips that fit over rungs. These are vital to the safe use of these ladders and, therefore, must again be regularly inspected.

The simple wooden pole ladder must be checked to ensure that the wire ties beneath certain rungs are in place and tight. Rungs must be checked to ensure they are still firm and do not twist, and the stiles checked to ensure they are not split or twisted.

All work equipment has the potential to be the cause of accidents. Obviously, the potential and the consequences differ between types of equipment.

Management systems for the training and instruction of operators, the inspection of equipment and the recording of those inspections, must be in place and complied with.

For further information on the selection and use of ladders and stepladders refer to Chapter D03 Common access equipment.

www.

For further guidance refer to the Health and Safety Executive (HSE) leaflet *Safe use of ladders and stepladders.*

C
05

5.5 Abrasive wheels

- Abrasive wheel machines of all types have the potential to cause severe injury if they are not used with care.
- Anyone who uses an abrasive wheel machine must be trained and competent to do so.
- The potential for danger arises not so much from the machine itself but from the grinding wheel or cutting-off disc used with the machine.
- Many accidents are caused by the abrasive wheel being rotated faster than its design speed, which results in it breaking up (bursting) at high speed.
- It is essential to check the compatibility of the abrasive wheel or cutting-off disc with the machine to which it is fitted.
- The fitting of any abrasive wheel or cutting-off disc to a machine (mounting) must only be carried out by someone who is trained and competent to do so.
- The person who is trained and competent to mount abrasive wheels or cutting-off discs need not be the same person who is competent to operate the machines.
- Using an abrasive wheel machine has the potential to cause occupational health problems and usually the wearing of appropriate PPE will be required.

Abrasive wheels are potentially dangerous if not used correctly. Most accidents result from selecting the wrong type of wheel or from over speeding. It is essential that:

- the right abrasive wheel for the job is chosen
- it is correctly mounted by a competent person on a compatible machine
- it is run at the correct speed and guards are fitted
- eye protection is used.

In most circumstances abrasive wheels rotate at very high speeds and contact with the revolving wheel can cause serious injury. When using a grinding wheel, a stream of hot, abrasive particles is thrown off, which can cause injury, particularly to the eyes. Finally, there is always a risk of the wheel disintegrating or bursting as it revolves. Fragments of the wheel can be projected a great distance, at great speed and in all directions.

5.5.1 Types of abrasive wheel

An abrasive wheel is generally defined as a wheel, cylinder, disc or point having abrasive particles, and intended to be power driven. It may consist entirely of abrasive particles, or be of metal, wood, cloth, felt, rubber or paper, with a surface covered with abrasive material. It may also be formed of a ring or segments of abrasive materials. These types of abrasive wheels are used for shaping material via grinding operations.

Other types of abrasive wheel are those used for cutting rather than grinding operations. These are circular metal blades, usually with diamond impregnated tips, used for cutting through concrete, steel, and so on.

5.5.2 Choosing the correct wheel

Two-thirds of accidents involving abrasive wheels are the result of using the wrong type of wheel for the job in hand. Had the manufacturer's recommendations been complied with then all these accidents would have been avoided.

Abrasive wheels should comply with the requirements of BS EN 12413 and BS ISO 525.

Many types and grades of abrasive wheel are available, and the correct selection is important. As a general rule, soft grade wheels are most suitable for use on hard materials and hard grade wheels are for use on soft materials. Coarse grains are for the rapid removal of material and fine grains are for polishing.

The use of an unsuitable wheel may result in the wheel face becoming loaded as the pores are clogged by the material being removed. If the wheel is too hard or too fine it may become glazed or polished. The consequence, in both cases, may be that the operative will press too hard, in an attempt to get the work done, and cause the wheel to break.

It is important that only reinforced, resin-bonded abrasive wheels should be used with portable grinding machines.

Abrasive wheels should be marked to conform to Annex A of BS EN 12413.

www.

For further guidance refer to the HSE publication *Safety in the use of abrasive wheels.*

5.5.3 Maximum permissible speed

The maximum permissible speed in revolutions per minute (rpm) and metres per second (m/s) specified by manufacturers should be marked on every abrasive wheel larger than 80 mm in diameter, or on the blotter or identification label that is sometimes attached to it. Since it is not practicable to mark smaller wheels, the maximum permissible speed in rpm of wheels 80 mm in diameter or less should be stated in a notice posted in a position where it can easily be read. For speeds of 50 m/s and above, colour coded stripes will appear on the wheel.

5.5.4 Restrictions of use

Annex A of BS EN 12413 and BS ISO 525 specify how wheels should be marked to indicate specific restrictions for use.

- RE1: Not permitted for hand-held and manually guided grinding.
- RE2: Not permitted for hand-held cutting-off machines.
- RE3: Not suitable for wet grinding.
- RE4: Only permitted for totally enclosed working areas.
- RE6: Not permitted for face grinding.

5.5.5 Shelf life

All organic bonded wheels for hand-held applications will bear a use-by date of three years from the date of manufacture.

5.5.6 Traceable number

A code number should be marked on the wheel to indicate the source and manufacturing details of the wheel.

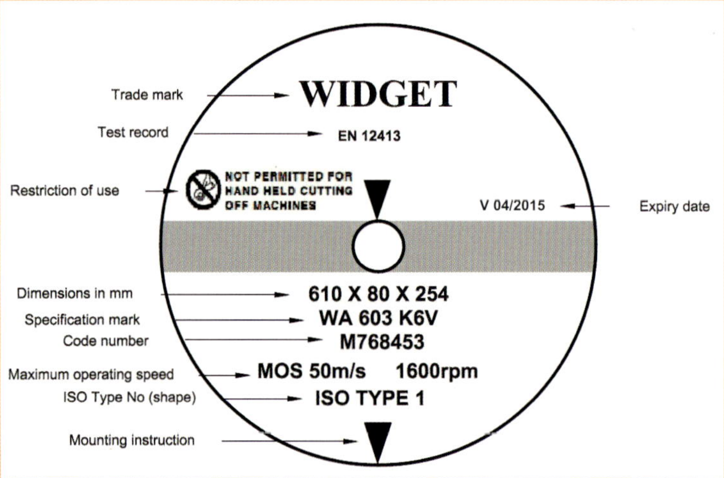

Abrasive wheel marking

5.5.7 Wheels bursting

The two main causes of abrasive wheels bursting are over-speeding and the incorrect mounting of the wheel.

5.5.7.1 Over-speeding

Abrasive wheels must not be run in excess of the maximum permissible speed recommended by the manufacturer. This should be clearly marked in rpm on all wheels over 80 mm (approximately three inches) in diameter.

For smaller wheels, a notice stating the maximum speed permissible should be displayed on or adjacent to where the machine is being operated. Any type of record may be kept, from computer database to a written record. The only restrictions are that a hard copy of the information must be available on request.

Speed of spindle. Every power-driven machine for use with abrasive wheels should have a notice fixed to it, specifying the maximum and minimum spindle speeds.

Machines that are not marked with their spindle speed must **not** be used.

Sometimes these markings are very small. If this is the case, consideration should be given to painting or engraving the spindle speed clearly on the machine.

Always keep the markings clean and in good condition so that they are easy to read.

Care must be taken to see that the maximum speeds are never exceeded. Governors, or other devices to control or limit speed, must be properly maintained and in good working order.

The speed of wheels may be checked using stroboscopic timing lights.

Peripheral speeds. Care must be taken to operate the wheel at the optimum speed recommended by the manufacturer.

As an abrasive wheel wears down, its peripheral speed is reduced and this, in turn, reduces its efficiency.

A wheel operated at too low a speed will not cut properly and there will be a tendency to press the work piece hard against the wheel. This may damage the wheel and cause it to burst.

5.5.7.2 Mounting of wheels

In order to be able to demonstrate compliance with legislation, abrasive wheels should only be mounted by a trained and competent person appointed to this duty by their employer.

5.5.8 Maintenance

In addition to checks immediately before and after each use, every machine should be regularly and frequently serviced by a competent person in accordance with the manufacturer's instructions. A record of this maintenance should be kept.

It is good practice to record the type and serial number of all abrasive wheel machines in a maintenance log, together with the date each machine is due for service. When servicing has been carried out, ensure that details of any completed work are entered in the log, together with the date that the next service is due.

All records should be kept up to date.

5.5.9 Training

Training for the **mounting** of abrasive wheels must only be given by a competent person, which often involves attending an external course. It must cover the grades, types and marking of wheels, the use, hazards, speeds, storage, handling, inspection, testing, dressing, adjustments and the functions of associated components (such as flanges, blotters, bushes and locking nuts).

WWW.

Details of suitable training courses and training providers can be found on the British Abrasive Federation's website.

5.5.10 Diamond blades

As with bonded abrasive wheels, people working with diamond blades must be properly trained and competent. Most of the safe procedures and precautions for using bonded abrasive wheels on hand-held machines apply to diamond blades. Additional advice and information can be obtained from suppliers and manufacturers.

Diamond blades are directional and must be mounted so that they rotate in the direction marked on the blade. They are designed to cut different materials, a requirement that must be strictly adhered to.

Diamond blades can significantly deteriorate and become unsafe if they are used to cut the wrong type of material. Reputable manufacturers provide inspection guides for their blades.

Use the correct equipment for the task

A worker used a concrete blade to cut a series of post holes through an asphalt surface to receive concrete fence posts. As a result the blade failed and several 50 mm long segment blade tips broke off at high speed, two of which embedded deep within his knee cap. He suffered high blood loss, was airlifted to hospital and the tips were removed during reconstructive surgery. He was off work for over six months and never fully recovered. Providing an additional asphalt blade would have avoided the accident.

Diamond blades can be used on hand-held machines at peripheral speeds of up to 100 m/s, provided that the machine is designed for this speed and the marked maximum permissible operating speed of the blade is not exceeded.

Under no circumstances must the blade be allowed to overheat.

Periodically, it may be necessary to redress the blade by making cuts in a special dressing block or abrasive block. These wheels can last a comparatively long time. Before use and with the power disconnected, make a special point of checking the condition of the spindle bearings, as these can deteriorate considerably during the lifetime of a diamond cutting wheel.

5.5.11 In-use considerations

5.5.11.1 Guards (fixed and hand-held machines)

- ☑ The guard should be designed, and be sufficiently robust, to contain any fragments in the event of the wheel bursting.
- ☑ The guard must be securely attached to the body of the machine, properly adjusted and maintained.
- ☑ The guard or shield supplied by the manufacturer must be adjusted to permit exposure of the minimum amount of wheel or disc to enable the job to be carried out. It must not be left off or altered in any way.

5.5.11.2 Defects

Employees are required to report any defects in work equipment, including abrasive wheels, guards or tool rests, to their employer.

5.5.11.3 Tool rests

Rests should be secured and adjusted so that they are as close as practicable to the wheel and no more than 3 mm away. If the gap between the wheel and the rest is too great, the work piece may become trapped and an accident may result.

It is good practice to continue to display cautionary notices concerning the dangers of abrasive wheels, wherever abrasive wheels are used or changed. This also serves as a useful reminder to employees of the training they have received.

5.5.12 Health considerations

5.5.12.1 Protection of eyes

During cutting or grinding processes, a stream of dust or abrasive particles and hot sparks is thrown off. These can cause serious injury to the eyes.

Because there is an obvious risk of eye injuries when an abrasive wheel is being used, eye protection should be provided in accordance with PPE Regulations (goggles, a face shield or visor, to BS EN 166).

For further information refer to Chapter B06 Personal protective equipment.

5.5.12.2 Respiratory protection

Depending upon what material is being cut, it is possible that the user of an abrasive wheel may be vulnerable to inhaling hazardous dust. With fixed machinery (such as bench grinders or fixed concrete saws) it may be possible to reduce airborne dust to a safe level by the following measures.

- ☑ Installing a fixed local exhaust ventilation system (for example, in workshops).
- ☑ Purchasing abrasive wheel machines that incorporate a facility for wet cutting or the attachment of a standalone dust extraction/collection unit.

If such dust suppression measures are not practical, it will be for the employer, or the person to whom the responsibility is delegated, to assess the hazardous nature of the dust and provide suitable respiratory protective equipment (RPE), consulting a supplier of PPE if necessary to establish what is needed.

For further information refer to Chapter B06 Personal protective equipment.

5.5.12.3 Vibration

The very nature of carrying out grinding or cutting work using abrasive wheels is likely to subject the person doing the job to a degree of hand-arm vibration. In extreme cases, hand-arm vibration can lead to permanent and disabling injuries. Employers must assess the risk to employees who carry out such work and put preventative and protective measures in place to ensure that the health of employees who carry out this type of work is not adversely affected.

For further information on control of vibration refer to Chapter B14 Vibration.

5.5.12.4 Noise

Grinding and cutting operations using abrasive wheel machines will inevitably result in an increased level of noise, both from the machine itself (for example, a petrol-driven disc cutter) and from contact between the cutting disc or grinding wheel and the material being worked upon. In many cases, the level of noise generated will exceed the lower exposure action value, meaning that, unless other control measures can be put in place, personal hearing protection must be made available and worn. Depending upon the level of noise and the proximity of other people, it may be necessary for them also to wear the hearing protection.

For further information on control of noise refer to Chapter B13 Noise.

5.5.13 Safety considerations

- The machine must have an efficient starting and stopping device that is easy to get to and can be readily operated.
- The floor area of the workplace must be kept in good condition, free of loose material, and should not be slippery.
- Abrasive wheels should be properly stored, flat and preferably in their boxes, and in accordance with the manufacturer's guidance. Care must be taken to see that any labels are retained, and not soiled or defaced so as to make them illegible.

For detailed information on abrasive wheels refer to the HSE publication *Safety in the use of abrasive wheels* (HSG17).

5.6 Portable fixing tools

Portable fixing tools use the power of an explosive charge or a gas propellant (from cartridges or a gas canister) to drive a fixing device into position in a base material. They are particularly useful if there are a large number of repetitive fixings to be made, where a portable fixing tool reduces the time and labour expended in this area. However, the resemblance of the tools to the shape and action of a gun can lead to their misuse, especially by young and inexperienced workers.

They can be extremely dangerous if used incorrectly. Operatives must be trained and competent and be of a sufficiently mature and responsible disposition.

Poor technique, or the use of incorrect equipment, will result in poor or defective fixing. The tool, type of cartridge or fuel cell, type of fixing and the base material must all be compatible.

In most cases, items of additional PPE, in addition to helmet, boots and hi-vis, will have to be worn.

At the end of the job all unused cartridges must be accounted for.

It should always be remembered that portable fixing tools are potentially lethal if they are used recklessly or incompetently.

5.6.1 Cartridge-operated tools

A cartridge-operated tool works by using a firing cap or cartridge to provide propellant to drive a fixing home. These tools must not be used in areas where a flammable atmosphere or risk of dust explosion may exist. Listed below are the primary factors that will ensure the proper and safe use of cartridge-operated tools.

- Adequate information, instruction, training and supervision.
- Competent and responsible users, who are over 18 years old and are not colour blind.
- The compatibility of the base material, the type of fixing and the cartridge strength.
- Restricting access to the work area during fixing activities.
- The provision and use of appropriate PPE.
- Carrying out work in accordance with *Code of Practice for safe use* (BS 4078-1).
- Using cartridge-operated tools that comply with BS 4078-2.

High-powered cartridge-operated tools can exert the same velocity as a small firearm.

For further information refer to the *Cartridge-operated hand-held tools. Safety requirements. Fixing and hard marking tools* (BS EN 15895).

5.6.1.1 Types of tool

There are two main types of cartridge-operated tool.

- **Indirect-acting** where the driving force is transmitted to the fixing by means of the expanding explosive gas acting on a piston. These tend to be low power.
- **Direct-acting** where the explosive force of the cartridge acts directly on the fixing, driving it along the barrel into the wall or material. These tend to be high power.

5.6.1.2 Power level of tools

Cartridge tools are generally classed as high power and low power.

- **Low power** is defined as giving the pin a kinetic energy not greater than 3.5 m/kg/f and a velocity not greater than 98.5 m per sec.
- **High power** applies to any values greater than those above. Using high power tools can result in dangerous through-shoots. This is where the fixing is fired right through the material.

Most of the commonly available tools are low power and indirect acting. These are by far the safest. There are high-power tools for special applications, and some old, high-power (direct acting) tools are still in use.

Hammer-activated tools are nearly always low power.

Some modern tools have provision for varying the power level (within the low-power range) by means of an adjustment that changes the size of the gas expansion chamber. There are also interchangeable pistons for different fixings or depths of penetration. Tools incorporating these features require a smaller range of cartridges.

5.6.1.3 Safety devices

All tools should incorporate a contact pressure safety device, which prevents them being fired unless the muzzle is pressed hard against the workface. They should always incorporate a drop-firing safety device that prevents the tool from firing when it is dropped onto a hard surface.

In addition, some tools are also equipped with an unintentional firing safety device. This prevents the tool from firing if the trigger is pulled before the tool is pressed against the work surface.

It should only be possible to fire the tool when it is correctly pressed against the work surface.

5.6.1.4 Cartridges

Any premises or any place where the cartridges for a cartridge tool are stored should be secure, dry and cool, and may need to be licensed. Checks should be made with the local police station or Local Authority as to whether this is necessary and, if so, where such a licence can be obtained.

Cartridges are designed for specific brands or types of tool and are not interchangeable, even if they are of a similar type or appearance. They are available in different strengths. It is preferable to start with a lower strength cartridge for a test fixing and then change to a more powerful cartridge if the depth of penetration is not sufficient.

BS 4078 requires the strength of the cartridges to be marked on the packaging and each cartridge to be colour coded to indicate its strength.

The colour codes set out in BS 4078 are shown below.

Cartridge strength	Colour
Extra low (XL)	Brown
Low (L)	Green
Low/medium (LM)	Yellow
Medium (M)	Blue
Medium/high (MH)	Red
High (H)	White
Extra high (XH)	Black

It should be noted that the code is not universally followed, and that colour coding alone must never be relied on as an indicator of the cartridge strength. Cartridges should be retained in the packaging (which identifies their strength) and not carried loose. Both cartridges and fixing nails are now available on plastic strips.

Proper controls must be put in place to account for all dispensed and unused cartridges. Fully dispensed cartridges in single or strip form are not classed as hazardous waste and can be disposed of in accordance with normal rules of non-hazardous waste.

Unused or unserviceable cartridges that cannot be fired are hazardous and in no circumstances should be exposed to fire or heat, or be subject to mechanical impact.

For the purpose of waste classification, unused cartridges often have a hazardous European waste code entry of *16 04 01* Waste ammunition*, but this should be checked in each case from the safety data provided by the supplier of the cartridge.

The supplier should be contacted to discuss suitable arrangements for the return/disposal of any unused or unserviceable cartridges. Cartridges should be returned to their original packaging so that they can be properly identified.

5.6.1.5 Suitability of base materials

Attempting to fix into unsuitable materials with cartridge tools is dangerous. Before firing the first fixing, a simple test should be made by driving a fixing of the intended type into the base material with a hammer. The result will show whether the material is suitable. No attempt should be made to fix into unsuitable materials. The table below provides general guidance.

Material	Result	Conclusion
Plaster, plywood and lightweight blocks	Sinks in easily	Too soft
Marble, some rock, hardened steel and weld metal	Fixing blunted	Too hard
Glass, glazed tiles, slates and some cast-iron	Material cracks or shatters	Too brittle
Sound wood, concrete and mild steel	Clear impression of fastener point	Suitable

C 05

5.6.1.6 Hazards in use

Hazards from the use of cartridge tools generally arise from one or more of the following three factors.

- Lack of competence, knowledge or training.
- Misuse, whether this be deliberate or due to ignorance of proper use.
- Poor maintenance, rendering the equipment defective or unsafe.

Two conditions that specially need to be guarded against are **through-penetration**, where the fixing goes through the material emerging in free flight on the other side, and **ricochet**, possibly towards the operator, where the fixing is deflected after firing.

5.6.1.7 Causes of through-penetration

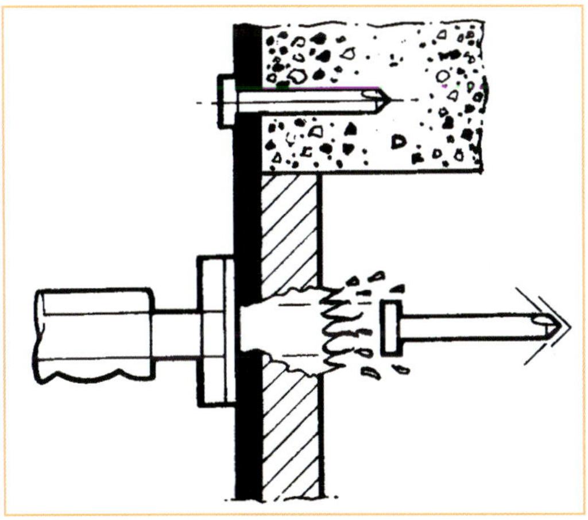

Penetration due to a change in the type of material

- Cartridge too powerful for the job being undertaken.
- Fixing into voids in the structure.
- The material being fixed into is too thin.
- Changes in the type or consistency of the material being penetrated.
- Not establishing the density of the material being fixed into.

To avoid these hazards:

- check the suitability of the material for cartridge-fired fixing
- if necessary, make a trial fixing using a low-powered cartridge
- check the area behind the material or structure into which the fixing is being fired, and guard the area so as to prevent the access of unauthorised persons
- use an indirect acting tool.

5.6.1.8 Causes of ricochet

Ricochet due to firing too near to edge

- Firing into the hole of a previously attempted fixing.
- Attempting to fix into excessively hard materials (such as hardened steel or welded areas).
- Cartridge tools not held square onto the work surface, causing the pin to strike at an angle and then be deflected.
- Attempting to fix too near to an edge.
- Hitting a reinforcing rod or dense aggregate hidden just under the surface.

To avoid ricochets:

- fixings should be at the recommended distance (or greater) from failed attempts
- do not fix into unfamiliar materials without first checking their suitability for cartridge fixing
- tools should be at right angles to the work surface. The whole rim of the splinter guard should be firmly placed against the workface so as to stabilise the tool and not leave gaps.

The risk of ricochet is reduced by the use of low-powered, indirect acting tools. If high-powered tools are used, there is a risk that the fixing can be deflected and come back towards the operator.

C 05

5.6.1.9 General precautions

Recoil of a cartridge tool can lead to loss of balance if working from an unstable workplace. In this instance, only low-power tools should be used. Operators not familiar with cartridge tools, or with the type of tool to be used, should test the tool for recoil before use. In all circumstances, an adequate and safe footing is a necessity. Makeshift platforms should not be used.

In the event of a **misfire**, the cartridge tool should be kept pressed in position against the workface for at least 30 seconds, to allow for any delayed detonation. Following this time period, the cartridge must then be removed strictly in accordance with the manufacturer's instructions. Cartridges that have misfired should be stored in a metal box and returned to the supplier.

Misfired cartridges should not be removed from the tool by levering under the rim. Some types are rim detonated and could be fired by this action. Only the proper extraction tool, as supplied by the manufacturer, should be used.

Loading of tools should be carried out immediately prior to use. Once the tool is loaded, it must never be pointed towards other people or at any part of the operator's body. Unused cartridges must be removed from the tool as soon as possible.

Storage and issue of tools. Only responsible and competent persons should supervise and check the acquisition, issue, use, return and maintenance of cartridge-operated tools.

Cartridge-operated tools and cartridges should be stored in a place that is secure, dry and cool. The issue of such tools and cartridges should be strictly controlled, and licensed if necessary. The following points should be clearly noted and understood.

- Cartridge tools should only be stored in an unloaded state.
- Different strengths of cartridge should be clearly identified and kept separate.
- The use of different makes of equipment on one site should be limited as far as possible.
- The manufacturer's instructions on the safe use of the cartridge tool should be available.

Personal protective equipment, complying with the relevant British Standards, should be used by operatives using cartridge-operated and gas-operated tools.

- Eye protection to BS EN 166-B must be provided and worn at all times when handling cartridge-operated tools, their cartridges or gas-operated tools.
- Noise levels will vary with the make of tool but all tools create a high intensity, short duration noise, so suitable hearing protection should be worn.
- Safety helmets to BS EN 397 should be worn while cartridge tools are in use.

The safety of other persons in the vicinity of where cartridge-operated or gas-operated tools are being used, a factor which should have been covered in the risk assessment, must be considered and all necessary precautions taken.

For further information refer to Chapter B06 Personal protective equipment.

5.6.2 Gas-powered tools

Lighter duty gas-powered tools can be used for the fixing of timber and other low density materials. These fixing tools are generally lighter in weight and use a battery and fuel cell, either propane or other gas, to act as a propellant rather than a cartridge. The fuel cell, typically a small aerosol canister, is mounted within the tool. The safety issues that need to be considered when using a gas-powered tool are shown below.

- ☑ Operators must be trained. Usually this can be provided by the supplier of the equipment. Operators must also be in possession of the relevant equipment instructions with which they must be familiar.
- ☑ The tool and the fuel cells must not be exposed to extremes of heat nor used within a flammable atmosphere.
- ☑ Harmful fumes are expelled during use and therefore the tool should be used in a well-ventilated area.
- ☑ When firing, the operator must be in a stable position and holding the tool at right angles to the work.
- ☑ Firing must not take place when others are behind the work. As with cartridge tools, through-penetration can occur.
- ☑ If a malfunction occurs the tool can usually be fired again (unlike when using a cartridge tool). However, the manufacturer's instruction manual should be consulted.
- ☑ Because of the mode of operation and speed of use, the tool can become hot. Reference should be made to warnings of hot areas on the tool.
- ☑ Fuel cells are a pressurised container and the propellant will remain in the fuel cell.
- ☑ Fuel cells must not be damaged, pierced, punctured, burnt or opened, even after use.
- ☑ Fuel cells should be disposed of in accordance with local regulations for aerosol products.

5.7 Woodworking machines

- ☑ Woodworking machines are classified as work equipment and must therefore comply with certain legal requirements.
- ☑ Many items of woodworking equipment, with their partially exposed blades or cutters, have the potential to cause serious personal injury if they are not properly used and maintained.
- ☑ Users of woodworking machinery must be trained on each type of machine that they are required to operate and be judged as competent by their employer.
- ☑ Hand-held, bench-mounted and free-standing woodworking machines can all be found on sites; all types present particular hazards to the operator and, in some cases, other people.
- ☑ The use of woodworking machines also has the potential to cause occupational health problems if appropriate preventative measures are not taken.

Several hundred accidents on different types of woodworking machinery are reported annually to the HSE. Of these, approximately 40% occur on circular saws and 25% on planing machines, both of which may be in use on construction sites. Woodworking machine cutters can inflict very serious injuries and it is essential that the regulations for guarding them are strictly observed. Neglect or ignorance of the regulations governing the use of such machinery creates the conditions in which accidents occur.

This chapter makes particular reference to circular saws and planing machines, since these are most commonly used on site in the construction industry.

5.7.1 Types of machine

The following non-exhaustive list gives examples of different types of woodworking machine.

- ☑ Circular saws.
- ☑ Sanding machines.
- ☑ Bandsaws.
- ☑ Routing machines.
- ☑ Planing/thicknessing machines.
- ☑ Chainsaws.
- ☑ Mortising machines.
- ☑ Tenoning machines.
- ☑ Vertical spindle moulding machines, including high-speed routing machines.
- ☑ Multi-cutter moulding machines having two or more cutter spindles.
- ☑ Trenching machines.
- ☑ Boring machines.
- ☑ Automatic and semi-automatic lathes.

5.7.2 Health risks

Some examples of occupational health problems caused by using woodworking machines are shown below.

- **Deafness, caused by exposure to noisy working environments.**
- **Hand-arm vibration syndrome, caused by vibration of equipment.**
- **Respiratory problems, caused by the inhalation of dust.**
- **Dermatitis, caused by contact with toxic wood.**

5.7.2.1 Noise-induced hearing loss

Woodworking machines can be particularly noisy when in use and the noise generated will be a significant hazard to health unless adequately controlled. Ideally, the level of noise will be controlled by means other than issuing PPE (for example, using screening or anti-vibration mountings).

For further information on control of noise refer to Chapter B13 Noise.

5.7.2.2 Hand-arm vibration syndrome

In the context of using woodworking machines, the predominant problem is considered to be hand-arm vibration. The necessary training and health surveillance should be implemented to prevent occurrence.

5.7.2.3 Respiratory problems

Woodworking machines inevitably produce dust that may affect the operator and persons in the vicinity. Dust should be treated and assessed in accordance with the COSHH Regulations. It should be controlled by effective extraction, collection systems or using dampening techniques in addition to wearing face-fitted RPE. Fumes can also be generated from adhesives and substances used for the treatment or finishes of the wood.

For further information on control of dust refer to Chapter B10 Dust and fumes.

5.7.2.4 Eye injury

Depending on the machine being used and the nature of the work being carried out, it may be necessary for machine operators (and possibly anyone assisting them) to wear eye protection (such as goggles) or a full face shield of a suitable impact-resistant grade.

5.7.2.5 Dermatitis

It may be necessary to provide operatives with suitable gloves to protect against skin damage whilst handling woods, particularly unplaned timber. Furthermore, the skin of a small number of persons is adversely affected by the natural oils that occur in some woods, notably cedar.

For further information refer to Chapter B06 Personal protective equipment.

5.7.3 Controls

Every machine must be fitted with start and stop controls that can be quickly and easily operated by the machinist.

5.7.4 Braking

An essential safety feature of most woodworking machinery is the provision of an automatic brake. This is to ensure that, if there is a risk of an employee coming into contact with tooling during the rundown period, the machine stops within 10 seconds or less, as defined by CEN standards.

All work equipment should be provided with the necessary controls that bring the equipment to a safe condition in a safe manner. To achieve this, a risk assessment should be carried out to determine whether the rundown time should be reduced and the retrofitting of brakes to a machine is necessary. Retrofitting should have been completed by 5 December 2008.

www.

For further information on the retrofitting of brakes refer to the HSE woodworking information sheet *Retrofitting woodworking machine brakes* (WIS 38).

5.7.5 Guarding cutters

Cutters include saw blades, chain cutters, knives, boring tools, detachable cutters and solid cutters. Cutters must be guarded to the greatest practicable extent, having regard to the work being done.

Guards must be of substantial construction, properly secured and adjusted, and maintained constantly in position while cutters are in motion.

Adjustments must not be made to any guard whilst the cutters are in motion, unless safe means (that is mechanical adjusters) are provided for those adjustments to be made.

The shape and size of guards may change as technology develops alternative safeguards, if these are at least as effective as before.

Every dangerous part of any woodworking machine must be securely fenced, unless it is in such a position or of such construction that it is as safe to every person on the site as it would be if it were fenced.

5.7.6 Portable, electrically powered saws

Portable, electrically powered saws should always be disconnected from the electrical supply before any adjustments, repairs, cleaning or any type of maintenance is carried out.

Whenever possible, to reduce the risk from electric shock, all portable, electric tools should operate from a 110 volt supply and be earthed or double insulated. The mains input to the 110 volt transformer should be protected by a residual current device (RCD), commonly known as a power breaker.

Portable, electrically powered saws must never be carried by their supply cable and, when operating, the supply cable must always be kept clear of the saw blade. The power plug must be examined each time, prior to use, for damage and security of the cable and all electrically powered saws should be examined regularly by a competent electrician.

Care should be taken to ensure that the spring loaded, lower blade guard returns to cover the blade after every cut. This guard, also known as the swivel guard, is designed to uncover the saw teeth when material is being cut then automatically covers the saw teeth when the saw is withdrawn. This guard must never be wired in the open position.

5.7.7 Chainsaws

Due to their high potential to cause injury, the use of chainsaws on building and construction sites is not generally recommended. While they are not illegal, site rules may prohibit their use.

Where chainsaws are used on site, they must be used only by operatives who are fully competent, have received specific and nationally approved training, and who are certificated to carry out the intended operation.

A specific risk assessment should be carried out for the operation and a written method statement produced covering the operation, including the need for full PPE, safe working at heights and, if necessary, a workplace safely away from other workers.

www.

For specific guidance on the use of chainsaws refer to the HSE leaflet *Chainsaws at work* (INDG317).

5.7.8 Other woodworking equipment

www.

For guidance on the safe use of other specific types of woodworking equipment refer to the HSE woodworking information sheets, which can all be downloaded, without charge, from its website.

- ☑ ***Circular saw benches – Safe working practices* (WIS 16).**
- ☑ ***Safe use of hand-fed planing machines* (WIS 17).**
- ☑ ***Safe use of vertical spindle moulding machines* (WIS 18).**
- ☑ ***Safety in the use of narrow band saws* (WIS 31).**
- ☑ ***Safe use of power-operated cross-cut saws* (WIS 35).**
- ☑ ***Safe use of manually operated cross-cut sawing machines* (WIS 36).**
- ☑ ***Safe use of woodworking machinery (L114).***

C 05

5.8 Compressors

Air compressors are used in construction as a power source for a range of tools and equipment. They can be either diesel or electric powered, trailer mounted or static, and range in output from 60 cfm* to 900 cfm, with working pressures of between seven and 12 bar (100 to 170 psi).

* cfm = cubic foot per minute of free air delivered.

5.8.1 Selection

When selecting a compressor for a particular application the following points should be taken into account.

- ☑ How many tools are going to be run from the compressor?
- ☑ What is the total airflow required?
- ☑ What is the working pressure required?
- ☑ Does the compressor need to be trailer mounted for ease of movement?
- ☑ Where will the compressor be located?
- ☑ Are diesel fumes an issue?
- ☑ Are there any noise limitations?
- ☑ How long will the compressor be required?

C
05

5.8.2 Compressed air safety

A compressed air system presents a range of hazards.

- ☑ Unintended release of pressure from the air receiver, piping or a loose hose-tool connection.
- ☑ Hoses that become disconnected from a tool, whipping in an uncontrolled fashion.
- ☑ Noise from compressed air leaks and pneumatic machinery.
- ☑ Hand-arm vibration from pneumatic tools (this is also a hazard with electric tools).
- ☑ Hot discharge pipes.
- ☑ Moving parts of compressor.
- ☑ Trip hazard from trailing air hoses.

Some ways to reduce the risks associated with the use of compressors and air tools are shown below.

- ☑ Ensure that users are trained in safe working practices and activities are supervised.
- ☑ Wear the correct PPE.
- ☑ Select low vibration tools from reputable suppliers.
- ☑ Ensure that guards protecting the belt and pulley drive are in place.
- ☑ Provide adequate ventilation.
- ☑ Fit a safety valve, pressure gauge and drain cock to air receivers.
- ☑ Fit anti-whip checks across all hose connection points.
- ☑ Consider replacing quick disconnect hose connections with safer two-stage disconnect components.
- ☑ Maintain a written scheme of examination, as required by the Pressure Systems Safety Regulations.

When compressed air is misused, it can cause serious injury or even death

A boilermaker was making repairs on a boiler. Upon emerging from the firebox, he disconnected the air hose from a riveting gun and began to blow dust from his clothes. There was one spot on his jacket sleeve that was so embedded in the fabric that the air did not readily remove it. In order to direct more air into the spot, he placed his index finger over the end of the air hose to partially close the opening. Air entered his finger through a small puncture wound, causing swelling and pain. Foreign material, apparently made up of dust and soot from the air, and oil from the compressor, was later removed from the wound. Even with proper medical treatment, gangrene set in and the finger had to be amputated.

As shown by this accident, using compressed air to blow dust or dirt off clothing or the body is a very dangerous practice. A strong blast of air can dislodge an eye from its socket, rupture lungs, intestines or an eardrum. Air forced into the bloodstream can even cause death.

For further guidance on the use, maintenance and examination of compressors and compressed air systems refer to the HSE publications *Safety of pressure systems* – Approved Code of Practice (L122) and *Compressed air safety* (HSG39).

5.9 Pumps

Pumps are used in the construction industry for a number of tasks (such as dewatering excavations, pumping bentonite for diaphragm walls and pumping sludge or sewage). Pumps can be diesel, electric or air powered and range in capacity from around 2 m^3/hr to 1,200 m^3/hr. They may be trailer or skid mounted and available in silenced versions, and are also available as submersible units.

5.9.1 Selection

When selecting a pump for a particular application the following points should be taken into account.

- ✓ What type of fluid is being pumped?
- ✓ What is the flow required?
- ✓ What are the suction and delivery heads required?
- ✓ Does the pump need to be trailer mounted for ease of movement?
- ✓ Where will the pump be located?
- ✓ Are diesel fumes an issue?
- ✓ Are there any noise limitations?
- ✓ How long will the pump be required?

Providing the pump supplier with this information will assist in getting the correct pump for the application.

For detailed guidance on the safe use of concrete pumps refer to the Construction Plant-hire Association *Code of Practice for the safe use of concrete pumps* (BS 8476).

5.10 Training and competence of personnel

It is essential that all personnel involved in the planning, supervision and carrying out of tasks with plant or work equipment are adequately trained and competent for their role. For larger and more complex items of plant there are a number of nationally recognised card schemes, which provide evidence of training and, in the case of the Construction Plant Competence Scheme (CPCS), competence. It is however the responsibility of each employer to ensure that their employees and those working under their control are competent to undertake the tasks they have been allocated.

It is also important that plant operators and work equipment users are familiar with the specific machine they are operating. Plant and work equipment comes in many shapes and sizes with significant differences in control layouts and operating characteristics. It is therefore essential that operators are given adequate familiarisation on an unfamiliar type or model of machine or equipment before they begin operations. This is generally carried out by an experienced person employed by the equipment owner.

Records should be maintained for all familiarisation training, clearly indicating the make and model covered.

Details of the Construction Plant Competence Scheme (CPCS) can be found online.

5.10.1 Medical fitness

People who operate plant and use work equipment have the potential to injure both themselves and other people in the workplace and the surrounding area. Ensuring that construction plant operators and work equipment users are medically fit to operate is primarily an issue for their employers, who have a duty to ensure that any employee is physically and mentally capable of undertaking the tasks they are required to carry out. Others in the construction sector, such as principal contractors and sub-contractors, will also have an interest in ensuring that plant operators have an appropriate level of fitness.

For detailed guidance on medical fitness refer to the Strategic Forum for Construction Plant Safety Group best practice guide – *Medical fitness to operate construction plant*.

5.11 Maintenance, checks and inspections

Maintenance, checks and inspections of plant and work equipment are essential if they are not to deteriorate over time, break down and ultimately fail. All maintenance should be carried out by a competent person who is familiar with the equipment and has the knowledge and experience to detect and repair existing or potential faults. The maintenance should be in accordance with the manufacturer's instructions and carried out at the recommended intervals.

All plant and work equipment should have a pre-use check carried out daily or at the start of each shift and any defects reported to a supervisor. This is normally undertaken by the operator or user, who should be trained to carry out the checks.

In addition to pre-use checks, inspections should be carried out at appropriate intervals, either as part of the maintenance process or at more frequent intervals. The frequency of inspections should be guided by the manufacturer's instructions and will depend on assessment of the risk of failure of the equipment. The following points should also be considered.

- Type, class and complexity of equipment (some types require weekly maintenance, others less frequent maintenance).
- Frequency that a piece of work equipment is used (equipment in regular use will probably require more frequent maintenance than equipment used infrequently).
- Equipment's potential to cause serious harm (powered machinery with the potential to cause serious harm (for example, a circular saw) will require more regular attention than a hammer).
- Likely deterioration of work equipment when not in use.
- The environment that the equipment is used in (an excavator used in a civil engineering project (such as sea defence work during the winter) will have the potential to deteriorate faster than an identical machine used in a less hostile environment).

The results of all checks and inspections should be recorded and there should be a system in place to ensure that all reported defects are rectified and recorded.

Each item of plant or equipment should have a history file containing all records of checks, maintenance and inspection, so that maintenance trends can be established and adequate maintenance demonstrated in the event of an accident.

06

Mobile plant and vehicles

Contents

Supporting information

G: Checklists and forms

GT 700 Toolbox talks

Overview

In the five years from 2008-13 there were 28 fatalities in construction where someone was struck by a moving vehicle and 26 due to being trapped by something collapsing or overturning. A significant number of these fatalities were caused by mobile plant and the majority could have been avoided by effective planning and control of mobile plant operations, adequate checking, inspection and maintenance of the plant, and thorough training, assessment and briefing of personnel.

This chapter gives an overview of the legal requirements for mobile plant operations and the steps required to ensure that these obligations are met so that mobile plant can be used safely and efficiently.

6.1 Introduction

The use and movement of mobile work equipment, whether over site roads or within specific areas, involves different and continually changing hazards. These have the potential to cause harm, such as persons being struck or run over, or thrown from or crushed by moving plant or equipment.

Problems with mobile plant operations often occur because of poor communications, both during planning and briefing of operators.

6.2 Important points

- Many accidents occur with mobile plant because operations were not properly planned in advance.
- Mobile plant should only be operated by trained and competent persons who have been properly briefed on the task to be carried out.
- The rated capacity of any item of mobile plant must never be exceeded.
- Mobile plant designed for specific operations must only be used for those operations. The design limitations and permitted modes of operation specified by the manufacturer must be complied with.
- All mobile plant must be adequately maintained.
- All mobile plant must be subjected to a schedule of inspections and, where appropriate, thorough examinations.
- Attention must also be paid to site features, such as overhead cables, excavations, unstable ground conditions and traffic routes.
- Mobile plant, first supplied after 1 January 1995, must be CE marked and meet the essential health and safety requirements of the Supply of Machinery (Safety) Regulations. Consequently, most items of lifting equipment are designed to a harmonised European Standard (such as EN 474-5 for excavators, EN 1459 for telehandlers and EN 280 for mobile elevating work platforms (MEWPs)).

6.3 Legislative requirements

For a brief summary of the legislative requirements for mobile plant operations refer to Chapter C05 Plant and work equipment. For more detailed information on legislation refer to Section A: *Legal and management*.

6.4 Types of mobile plant

By definition, mobile plant is plant that moves around a construction site, generally under its own power, and is controlled by an operator. Mobile plant is sub-divided into the three areas listed below.

6.4.1 Ride-on plant

Ride-on plant is where the operator sits/stands on the machine or in a cab (examples being rollers, excavators, loading shovels, rough terrain cranes, crawler cranes, self-propelled MEWPs, telehandlers, road planers, asphalt spreaders and dumpers).

Plant that is not designed to carry passengers should be provided with a notice clearly stating 'No passengers'.

People can only be carried if the vehicle has been designed for such a purpose. Passengers and drivers must not be carried unless proper seating, strongly and correctly connected to the main structure of the vehicle, is provided.

Where passengers are permitted to be carried, additional restraining devices must be provided.

Where on-board work has to be carried out, seating should be provided, if possible, with work platforms fitted with suitable barriers or guard-rails to stop operatives falling from the equipment whilst it is in motion.

6.4.2 Pedestrian-controlled plant

This type of equipment relies heavily on the experience and competence of the operative for its safe operation. Small pedestrian-operated rollers, vibrating plate compactors and surface grinders are among the types of equipment within this category.

Common accidents involving pedestrian-controlled equipment occur when operators of small vibrating rollers are crushed between the machine and adjacent obstructions. This is one reason why the regulations require efficient stop controls to be fitted. It is also essential that operators are provided with, and wear, strong protective footwear to prevent their feet from being injured.

6.4.3 Lifting equipment

For further information on the lifting aspects of mobile plant that is also lifting equipment (such as mobile cranes, lorry loaders, MEWPs, telehandlers and excavators used for lifting) refer to Chapter C07 Lifting operations and Chapter C08 Lifting equipment.

6.5 Planning and use of mobile plant

The Management of Health and Safety at Work Regulations require that all tasks carried out at work are subject to a risk assessment to identify hazards and assess the risks associated with the task. Planning a safe site should begin before the construction phase. In accordance with the Construction (Design and Management) Regulations (CDM) there are specific duties placed on all of those involved within the construction process, including clients, principal designers, designers, principal contractors and contractors. The planning process for the use of mobile plant is similar to that for most other tasks and consists of the following steps.

Step 1	Identifying the task to be undertaken.
Step 2	Identifying the hazards associated with the task.
Step 3	Carrying out a risk assessment.
Step 4	Identifying control measures.
Step 5	Developing the method to be used.
Step 6	Recording the planning in a method statement (including any contingency activities for rescue).
Step 7	Communicating the plan to all persons involved.
Step 8	Reviewing the plan before the task starts and incorporating any changing circumstances.

6.5.1 Practical measures for safe workplaces

The following practical measures should be considered to ensure that mobile plant and equipment can be used safely on site.

- Pedestrian routes should be established on site to provide safe pedestrian access to work areas.
- Pedestrian routes should be segregated from mobile plant and vehicles, either by a safe distance or by physical barriers.
- Traffic routes should be planned in order to minimise congestion and risk of collision. These routes should be kept free of obstructions and properly maintained, with access points restricted and clearly marked.
- Appropriate speed limits should be introduced.
- One-way traffic systems should be implemented, if possible and appropriate.
- Parking places should be designated for delivery vehicles and other vehicles left temporarily on site.
- The operating area should be clear, as far as possible, on all sides.
- Where excavation is taking place, operators must know the location of any overhead power lines, underground cables, sewers, ducts or services before digging operations commence.
- Trenches and excavations should be fenced or otherwise guarded.
- Ground conditions should be stable and sufficiently level for the operations being carried out and the equipment used.
- Where equipment fitted with outriggers or stabilisers is used, the load-bearing capacity of the ground should be assessed so that the imposed loads do not exceed this capacity.

- Where site vehicles are employed in tipping material into excavations, baulks of timber or other effective blocks should be provided to prevent the vehicle over-running the edge.
- Excavations may have to be provided with extra support or shoring to prevent the weight of adjacent vehicles causing a collapse (surcharging).

For detailed guidance on the measures to be taken in planning for the use of mobile plant refer to the HSE guidance *The safe use of vehicles on construction sites* (HSG144) and *Protecting the public: your next move* (HSG151).

6.5.2 Material unloading and loading

Materials that are unloaded or tipped from plant should be deposited in planned locations where they will not cause an obstruction or hazard.

Marshallers safely reversing a delivery lorry. The driver can clearly see a marshaller in each wing mirror

A marshaller should assist the driver during any manoeuvring or tipping operation to ensure that it is safe to tip and that there are no other hazards to be encountered during the operation.

Operatives must not remain on vehicles that are being loaded unless the vehicle is equipped with an approved cab or falling object protective structures (FOPS). Consideration should also be given to additional precautions that may be required (for example, increased signage, entry and exit signs into and out of delivery areas, restricted pedestrian movement, proximity sensors and/or convex mirrors).

Operatives working with plant or vehicles, or on sites where there are regular vehicle movements, should be provided with the appropriate PPE, which should include high-visibility clothing.

6.5.3 Selection of mobile plant

Every employer must ensure that the work equipment is constructed or adapted to be suitable for the purpose for which it was provided.

In selecting the work equipment, every employer shall take account of the working conditions and the risks to the health and safety of persons who are in the vicinity of where the work equipment is to be used.

The design of some vehicles presents hazards (such as restricted visibility and lack of driver protection) from the effects of overturning, noise and vibration. Some old designs of site dumpers allowed the vehicle to be knocked easily into gear as the driver dismounted.

Choosing the right machine for the job is an essential part of effective mobile plant management. The equipment selected needs to be capable of performing its designated tasks safely. Some important factors to consider are given below.

- Stability under all foreseeable operating conditions (for example, ground and weather conditions).
- Safe access to and from the cab and other working locations on the vehicle.
- Effective braking systems.
- Adequate visibility for the driver all around the vehicle, especially when reversing.
- Headlights, a horn, windscreen wipers and warning devices (such as reversing alarms).
- Physical guards to protect dangerous parts (such as power take-off shafts, chain drives, trapping points and exposed exhaust pipes).
- Protection for the driver from work hazards (such as working at height and falling from the vehicle, falling objects and the effects of the vehicle overturning).
- Protection for the driver from the weather, noise, vibration, fumes and dust.

Manufacturers' specifications need to be considered when choosing vehicles for construction and civil engineering work. In particular, load and stability limits need to be taken into account when choosing vehicles for use on uneven and sloping ground. Some vehicles, especially those involved in lifting operations (such as some lift trucks and telescopic handlers) require flat, compacted surfaces to operate safely.

6.5.4 Braking systems

Effective braking systems, including parking brakes, are essential for the safe use of vehicles. In accordance with the Road Traffic Act parking brakes should be fitted on trailers over 0.75 tonnes maximum gross capacity. Where parking brakes are not fitted, trailer wheels need to be chained or locked to prevent movement when the trailer is parked. Wheel chocks should be used to prevent unintended vehicle and trailer movements when parked on sloping ground. Trailers with maximum gross weights between 0.75 tonnes and 3.5 tonnes should have at least an overrun brake (such as an inertia brake), while trailers over 3.5 tonnes should be fitted with braking systems linked to the towing unit.

6.5.5 Roll-over protective structures

Where there is the risk of mobile work equipment rolling over it should be fitted with roll-over protective structures (ROPS), such as reinforced cabs or a roll-cage, to stop falling mobile equipment doing anything more than falling onto its side, thereby minimising the risk of a person being crushed. The cabs or roll-cages should give adequate clearance for operatives to escape if the equipment does completely overturn.

Where there is a risk of an operator being thrown then crushed by equipment rolling over, a suitable restraining system (such as a seat belt) should be fitted **and worn by the operator**.

This requirement may also apply to equipment fitted with a fully enclosed cab if there is a risk of a person who is thrown from their seat being injured by coming into contact with the inside of the cab's structure.

Restraining systems must be fixed to a strong anchorage point on the main structure of the equipment.

In areas of limited access, ROPS may be removed only if a suitable and sufficient risk assessment has been carried out and there is no risk of overturning.

e.g. **Wearing seat belts**

Telehandler cabs are provided with seat belts to restrain the operator and reduce the risk of serious injury in the event of the machine overturning. A survey of telehandler accidents in the UK carried out by the Health and Safety Executive (HSE) shows that in seven years there were at least 72 lateral overturns of telehandlers. In three cases the operator was killed by being ejected from the cab and crushed; in a further two cases the operator was ejected from the cab and received serious crushing injuries. Had these operators been wearing their seat belts their deaths or injuries would probably have been avoided.

6.5.6 Falling object protective structures

ROPS and FOPS cab

Where there is the risk to persons operating mobile work equipment of being struck by falling material, overhead protection or a manufacturer's strengthened cab must be fitted to stop any falling material striking the operator.

6.5.7 Prevention of unauthorised start-up

It must not be possible for self-propelled mobile work equipment to be started by unauthorised persons when the vehicle is parked. Additionally, it must be possible to isolate the drive mechanism. This can be achieved by simple measures (such as the removal of ignition keys or starting handles), the use of more sophisticated systems (such as keypad or smart card isolators) or remotely controlled telematics systems.

6.5.8 Lighting and warnings

When self-propelled mobile work equipment is used in the dark or in reduced visibility, lights must be fitted and used to enable the work area to be adequately illuminated. In addition, amber flashing beacons that give warning of the presence of the vehicle should be fitted and used. It is required that some types of construction vehicles are fitted with audible reversing warning devices or similar devices (such as CCTV).

6.5.9 All-round visibility

Accidents involving mobile plant and pedestrians frequently involve poor visibility where the plant operator has not seen the pedestrian or bystander. Current standards aim to ensure that the operator of the plant or vehicle has all-round vision from the operating position. Therefore, plant needs to be assessed to ensure that the existing visibility meets the requirements of the PUWER Regulations.

! It is generally accepted that the operator should be able to see, at all times, an object positioned one metre above ground level and one metre away from the plant through 360° visibility.

All-round visibility

This can usually be achieved by the use of aids (such as additional mirrors, convex mirrors or CCTV).

Where this is not possible, consideration should be given to providing a competent, qualified banksman working exclusively with the plant operator and implementing exclusion zones to prevent unauthorised access into any danger zones. *(For further information on plant safe zones refer to 6.6.)*

6.5.10 Forward-tipping dumpers

Amongst mobile plant, forward-tipping site dumpers are worthy of special note because they are involved in a disproportionately high number of plant-related accidents. This applies to both rigid-frame and articulated dumpers.

Over 60% of dumper deaths involve the driver when the vehicle overturns. Most other deaths occur when pedestrians are struck by the dumper whilst it is in operation.

Forward-tipping dumper

The common causes of these accidents are shown below.

- Overturning on slopes, rough ground and at the edges of excavations.
- Travelling with a high-lift skip in the raised position.
- The driver failing to observe pedestrians who are then run over by the front wheels.
- The driver being thrown from the vehicle whilst travelling over rough ground.
- Driver error due to lack of experience and training, including accidental operation of the controls.

Efforts to reduce dumper accidents should focus on the following.

- Effective site management and control of how dumpers are operated generally.
- Selecting the correct machine for the job.
- Ensuring that machines are routinely inspected, serviced and withdrawn from use if unsafe.
- Ensuring that only trained, competent drivers are allowed to operate dumpers, which includes removing the key when not in use.
- Ensuring that site roads are suitable and safe for the use of dumpers.

For detailed guidance on the safe use of forward-tipping dump trucks refer to the HSE publication *Construction site transport safety: safe use of site dumpers* (Construction information sheet No. 52).

The HSE has produced an ACoP on rider-operated lift trucks, which outlines the main legal requirements of use (L117).

6.5.11 Quick hitches

The quick hitches fitted to excavators and other earthmoving plant make a valuable contribution to the construction process by enabling buckets and other attachments to be attached and detached rapidly, as required. Unfortunately there have been a significant number of accidents involving the use of quick hitches, which have included fatalities.

When using quick hitches some precautions (listed below) should be observed. These precautions are applicable to all types of quick hitch – manual, semi-automatic and all fully automatic types, including those that lock onto both pins. All types of quick hitch can be safely used by competent people within a safe system of work. This will involve planning, training, instruction, communication, supervision and maintenance. However, all types of quick hitch may fail if they are not used and maintained correctly.

Site management should familiarise themselves with the different types of quick hitches, and any related company policy, to assess and monitor what contractors should be doing to manage the risk.

- ☑ Keep other workers away from the machine's working range. Never work under the bucket or attachment and ensure that the operator isolates the controls if there are other workers in the machine's working range. Ensure that your site supervisors enforce this rule.
- ☑ Make sure that your operators are aware of their personal and legal responsibility to use all quick hitches safely. Serious misuse of quick hitches should always be treated as gross misconduct, which could well lead to dismissal or individual prosecution.
- ☑ Check that all operators confirm that the quick hitch is in place every time they change an attachment. It is essential that this is done by close inspection at the quick hitch, which will normally entail the operator getting down from the cab. It is good practice to make this a requirement for all quick hitches.
- ☑ Check that site supervisors understand that the operator has to fully confirm that the quick hitch is in place. Make sure site supervisors allow operators time to do this.
- ☑ Check that site supervisors monitor that operators are confirming proper engagement, by spot checks.
- ☑ Check that machines are in good order, and all quick hitches are included in the maintenance plan and subject to proper maintenance.
- ☑ Check that operators and maintenance personnel have specific instructions for the combination of machine, quick hitch and attachment.
- ☑ Confirm that operators are competent to use the specific quick hitch in accordance with the manufacturer's instructions and the safe system of work.
- ☑ Forbid practices (such as pick and place) that involve moving attachments without properly engaging the locking devices.

e.g. Using quick hitches with other attachments

Contractors may want to use quick hitches with attachments other than a bucket in normal configuration. However, if a specific application (such as the fitting of vibratory hammers or reversing of buckets) is not explicitly allowed by the manufacturer, the user should assume that it is not allowed, and should not use the quick hitch for this attachment or application. Quick hitches should only be used with attachments and in applications as specified by the manufacturer.

It is essential that operators get out of the cab to physically ensure that all quick hitches are securely locked before starting work with a newly attached attachment.

www.

For detailed guidance on quick hitches refer to the Strategic Forum for Construction's *Safe use of quick hitches on excavators* (Best practice guide).

6.5.12 Concrete pumps

All concrete pumping pours should be planned to ensure that they are completed safely and that all significant foreseeable risks have been taken into account. Planning should be carried out by personnel who have the appropriate expertise. In cases of repetitive concrete pours, this planning may only be necessary in the first instance, with periodic reviews to ensure that no factors have changed.

www.

For detailed guidance on the safe use of concrete pumps refer to the Construction Plant-hire Association's *Safe use of concrete pumps* (Good practice guide).

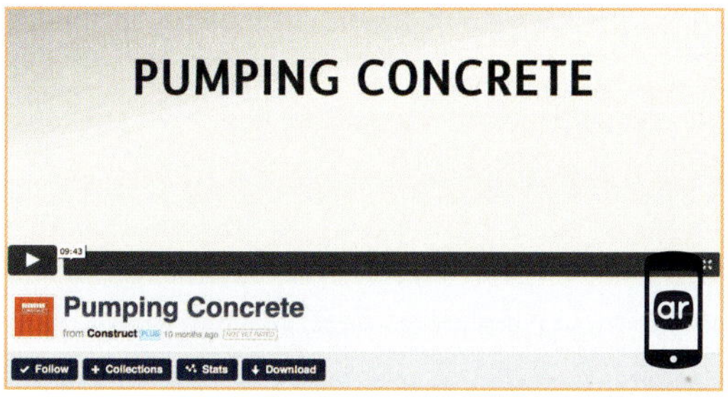

A video demonstrating the dangers of concrete pumping and pours; checks and inspections of pipelines; PPE; blockages and clearance of, and the cleaning out process, is available from Construct: Concrete structures group.

6.6 Plant safe zones

The following diagrams are for guidance purposes and give an understanding of the safe zones applicable to a range of plant machinery likely to be used on site.

- ☑ **Always signal the plant operator and receive a positive response before entering Zone 1.**
- ☑ **Keep out of Zone 2 at all times.**

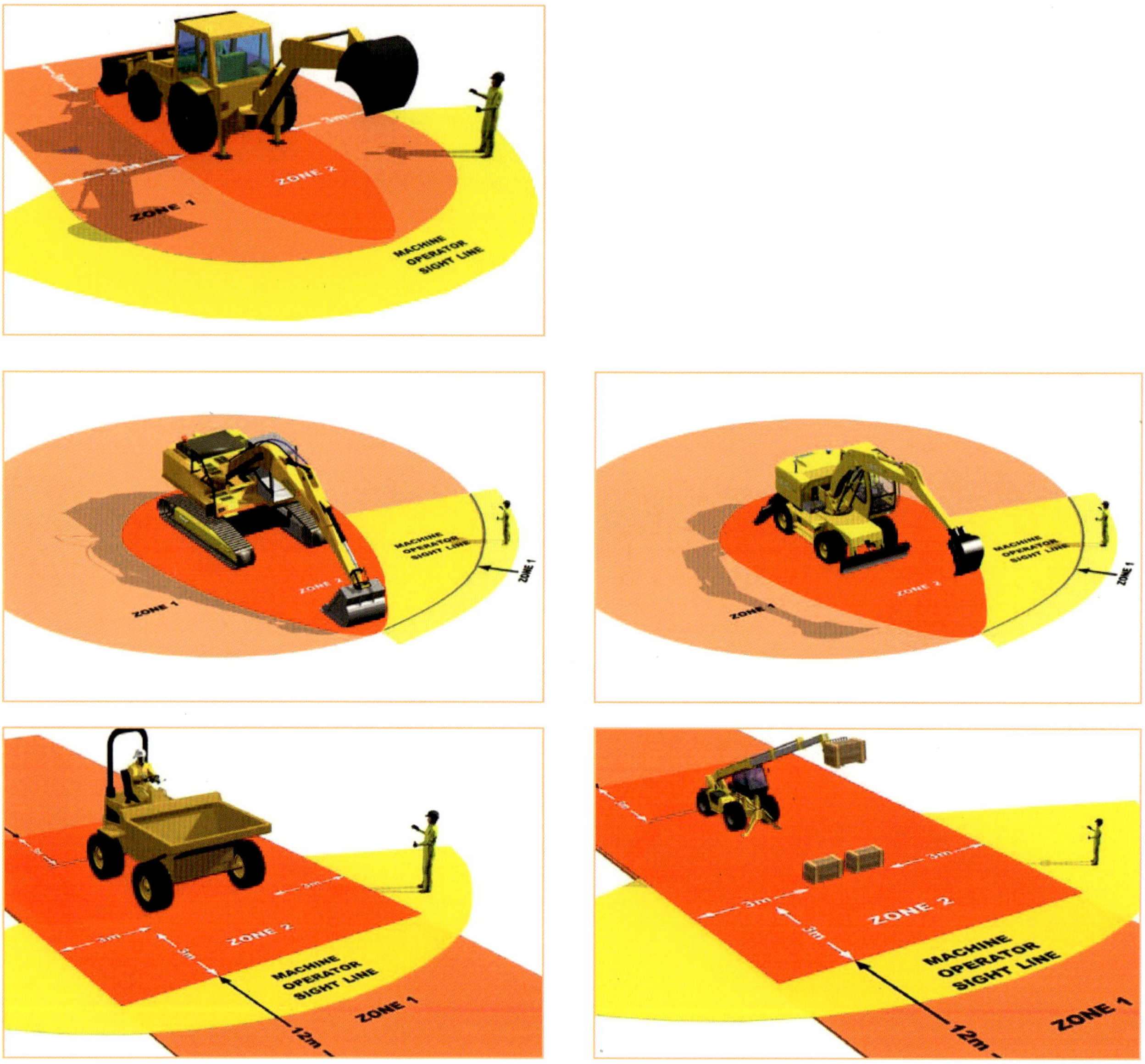

(Reproduced from the Delivery hub health, safety and environment – Raising the bar 1 – Plant and equipment document from the Highways Agency, under licence of the Controller of Her Majesty's Stationery Office.)

6.7 Training and competence of personnel

It is essential that all personnel involved in the planning, supervision and carrying out of mobile plant operations are adequately trained and competent for their role. There are a number of nationally recognised card schemes that provide evidence of training and, in the case of the Construction Plant Competence Scheme (CPCS), competence. It is, however, the responsibility of each employer to ensure that their employees and those working under their control, are competent to undertake the tasks they have been allocated.

It is also important that mobile plant operators are familiar with the specific machine they are operating. Mobile plant comes in many shapes and sizes, with significant differences in control layouts and operating characteristics. It is therefore essential that operators are given adequate familiarisation on an unfamiliar type or model of machine before they begin operations. This is generally carried out by an experienced person employed by the equipment owner.

Records should be maintained for all familiarisation training, clearly indicating the make and model covered.

Details of the Construction Plant Competence Scheme (CPCS) can be found online.

Worker's head struck with digger bucket

A construction worker has been prosecuted after he struck another worker on the head with the bucket on a digger. He was prosecuted after an investigation found he had been using a mobile phone, whilst operating the excavator vehicle on a building site, and had not noticed his colleague.

The construction worker was working alongside a colleague who was driving a site dumper truck. The operation involved excavating and dumping material into the truck for transport to another location at the site. The court heard that the driver of the dumper truck had returned to the excavation site to await the next load of material. The construction worker had been using his mobile phone and, not realising his colleague had returned, rotated the upper body of the excavator, causing the metal bucket to strike the driver on the side of his head.

The driver sustained multiple fractures to his jaw, as well as a punctured and collapsed lung. He was hospitalised for ten days and did not return to work until 14 months later, with further surgery still required on his jaw.

The construction worker was ordered to pay compensation of £2,500 to the injured worker, and costs of £1,554 after pleading guilty to a single breach of the Health and Safety at Work etc. Act 1974.

Speaking after the hearing, the HSE inspector said: 'Construction site vehicles are extremely powerful and, if the operator becomes distracted, can be highly dangerous. Road users are rightly banned from using mobile phones when driving cars. It's clearly important that those in control of machinery – weighing up to 40 tonnes in some cases – need to be equally attentive and concentrate solely on the job at hand. This incident could easily have been avoided if the operator had followed site rules and not become complacent about his responsibilities when operating his vehicle.' *(Source: HSE.)*

www.

For detailed guidance on plant operator competence refer to the Strategic Forum for Construction Plant Safety Group's *Competence to operate construction plant* (Good practice guide).

6.7.1 Medical fitness

People who operate plant have the potential to injure both themselves and other people in the workplace and the surrounding area. Ensuring that construction plant operators are medically fit to operate is primarily an issue for their employers, who have a duty to ensure that any employee is physically and mentally capable of undertaking the tasks they are required to carry out. Others in the construction sector (such as principal and sub-contractors) will also have an interest in ensuring that plant operators have an appropriate level of fitness.

www.

For detailed guidance on medical fitness refer to the Strategic Forum for Construction Plant Safety Group's *Medical fitness to operate construction plant* (Best practice guide).

6.7.2 Supervision

An essential part of the safe use of mobile plant is supervision of the plant operator. The responsibilities of the supervisor are, each day, to re-brief the operator and others on the task and ensure they are put to work safely.

- ☑ Reinforce the main elements of the safe system of work, including:
  - strict adherence to exclusion zones
  - the correct safe methods when fitting/removing attachments with a quick hitch
  - consulting the operator and others regarding any issues/comments they have in adhering to or the effectiveness of the safe system of work and, where appropriate, instigate changes.
- ☑ Check that the operator has undertaken the relevant daily checks.
- ☑ Check the required maintenance has been undertaken.
- ☑ Ensure the inspection/maintenance log/check sheet has been completed and signed. The supervisor's signature on the check list/log may be used as verification that they have carried out the check.

As part of the supervisor's ongoing duties, they must, throughout the day, monitor that the safe system of work is being adhered to, including maintenance of exclusion zones, that no-one is working below attachments at any time and quick hitches are being used as manufacturer's recommendations, including the correct use of any safety pins or locking devices.

The supervisor should regularly check that the manufacturer's manual for operating the machine is in the cab, that any relevant decals are displayed in the cab and/or on the machine and that the next service date by a fitter has not expired. The daily checklist for the machine will provide evidence of some of these points.

6.8 Maintenance, checks and inspections

Maintenance, checks and inspections of mobile plant are essential if it is not to deteriorate over time, break down and ultimately fail. All maintenance should be carried out by a competent person who is familiar with the equipment and has the knowledge and experience to detect and repair existing or potential faults. The maintenance should be in accordance with the manufacturer's instructions and carried out at the recommended intervals.

All mobile plant should have a pre-use check carried out daily or at the start of each shift and any defects reported to a supervisor. This is normally undertaken by the operator who should be trained to carry out the checks.

In addition to pre-use checks, inspections should be carried out at appropriate intervals, either as part of the maintenance process or at more frequent intervals. The frequency of inspections will depend on assessment of the risk of failure of the equipment and should be guided by the manufacturer's instructions.

The results of all checks and inspections should be recorded and there should be a system in place to ensure that all reported defects are rectified and recorded.

Each item of mobile plant should have a history file containing all records of maintenance, inspection and thorough examination, so that maintenance trends can be established and adequate maintenance demonstrated in the event of an accident.

For guidance on construction plant reception and inspection reports refer to Appendix A.

Appendix A – Construction plant reception and inspection report guidance

These guidance notes are provided to assist the persons appointed by the site manager to complete reports.

Mobile plant is defined as mechanical or electrical plant that is self-propelled. The types of plant typically covered by the mobile plant reception report are as follows.

- All types of excavator.
- All forward or rearward tipping dumpers/trucks.
- All types of cranes.
- All types of compacting rollers.
- Rough terrain forklift trucks.
- Tractors and their trailer units.

In the case of plant provided by a plant hirer, then, at the site manager's discretion, a competent person appointed by the plant hirer may conduct the inspection and complete the report.

In the case of plant owned or hired by a contractor, then a competent person employed by the contractor may conduct the inspection and complete the report.

All completed mobile plant reception reports shall be retained for inspection on site.

The report is produced in a checklist format for ease of use and is intended to provide a means by which the condition of all plant delivered to site can be checked by the appointed person. All questions shall record an answer, with a suitable comment or action included when necessary.

The appointed person is also required to confirm the validity of relevant statutory documentation (such as test certificates) thorough examination and inspection reports.

An aide memoir is provided below to assist the appointed person on statutory requirements that apply to certain items of plant.

Plant	Thorough examination	Comments	Documentation
All types of cranes used for lifting people and mobile elevating work platforms (MEWPS).	Current six-monthly thorough examination report.	▪ Fitted with suitable devices to prevent persons being crushed, trapped, struck or falling when riding or working from carrier. ▪ Provision of suitable devices to prevent risk of a carrier failing. ▪ Safe means of escape for persons trapped in a carrier.	Evidence of daily or weekly inspection and six-monthly thorough examination, including certification of a SWL.
Excavators used as cranes without any restriction and a fixed or variable SWL greater than one tonne.	Current 12-monthly thorough examination report.	▪ Fitted with controlled lowering devices (check valves). ▪ Provided with a properly fitted hook or lifting shackle marked with SWL. ▪ Supplied with a register for the weekly inspections of the excavator and, where fitted, safe load indicator. ▪ Have the SWL clearly marked on the machine or displayed in the cab.	Evidence of daily or weekly inspection and 12-monthly thorough examination, including certification of a SWL.
All types of cranes and excavators used as cranes without restrictions and a fixed SWL of one tonne or less.	Current 12-monthly thorough examination report.	▪ Provided with properly fitted hook or lifting shackle marked with SWL. ▪ Supplied with a register for weekly inspections of the machine and where fitted, a safe load indicator. ▪ Have the SWL clearly marked on the machine or displayed in the cab.	Evidence of daily or weekly inspection and 12-monthly thorough examination, including certification of a SWL.

Following completion of the report at receipt of the plant on site, formal inspection/examination must be repeated at least at the intervals specified by legislation or policy.

For a construction plant reception and inspection report form refer to Section G: *Checklists and forms*.

07

Lifting operations

Contents

Supporting information

G: Checklists and forms

GT 700 Toolbox talks

Overview

Each year there are, on average, six fatalities and a significant number of major and minor injuries in the construction industry due to lifting operations. In addition, there are many more incidents that lead to property, material and equipment damage, resulting in costly delays. The majority of these could have been avoided by effective planning and control of the lifting operations, adequate selection, maintenance, inspection and thorough examination of lifting equipment and thorough training, assessment and briefing of personnel.

This chapter gives an overview of the legal requirements for lifting operations and the steps required to ensure that these obligations are met so that lifting operations can be carried out safely and efficiently. The requirements for installing, using, checking, maintaining, inspecting and thoroughly examining specific types of lifting equipment and lifting accessories are covered in Chapter C08 Lifting equipment.

7.1 Introduction

Experience has shown that lifting operations can be a hazardous activity if not properly planned and carried out. Safe lifting operations will depend upon the following.

- ☑ The availability of suitable lifting equipment, which is properly maintained.
- ☑ The provision of adequate information, instruction, training or supervision for everyone involved.
- ☑ Thorough pre-planning of each lifting operation.
- ☑ Compliance with safe systems of work, as detailed in risk assessments and method statements (lifting plan).

Although regulations require that safe systems of work are developed, accidents occurring during lifting operations indicate that all too often these are not in place or, if they are, they are not complied with.

Lifting operations have the potential for death and serious injury to both site workers and members of the public off site. In addition to the terrible cost in human suffering, accidents have a financial cost. There is a very strong business case for improving safety performance.

Problems with lifting operations often occur because of poor communication, both during planning and when lifting.

7.2 Important points

- ☑ Many accidents occur during lifting operations because they were not properly planned in advance.
- ☑ All lifting operations must be carried out by, and under the control of, trained and competent persons who have been properly briefed on the lifting plan.
- ☑ The rated capacity of any item of lifting equipment or lifting accessory must never be exceeded.
- ☑ All lifting equipment and lifting accessories used for lifting operations must be adequately maintained.
- ☑ All lifting equipment and lifting accessories used for lifting operations must be subjected to a schedule of inspections and thorough examinations.
- ☑ In addition to the lifting equipment and lifting accessories used, attention must also be paid to site features (such as overhead cables, unstable ground conditions and adjacent properties).
- ☑ When using a hired crane, a contract lift will transfer the majority of the legal responsibility for carrying out the lifting operation in a safe manner to the contract lift company.

The collapse, overturning or failure of any load-bearing part of a hoist, crane or other lifting equipment is a notifiable dangerous occurrence, even if nobody is injured.

For further information refer to Chapter A13 Accident reporting and investigation.

C 07

7.3 Legislative requirements

A brief summary of the two main legislative requirements for lifting operations and lifting equipment are listed below.

For detailed information on legislation refer to Section A: *Legal and management* and for other related legislation refer to Chapter C05 Plant and work equipment.

7.3.1 Provision and Use of Work Equipment Regulations (PUWER)

PUWER is concerned with such matters as the selection of suitable work equipment, safeguarding of dangerous parts of machinery, provision of appropriate controls, training of operators and maintenance of work equipment, including cranes and lifting equipment.

PUWER places duties on any person who has control to any extent of any of the following.

- Work equipment.
- A person at work who uses, supervises or manages the use of work equipment.
- The way in which work equipment is used at work (including maintenance).

PUWER applies to employers in respect of work equipment provided for, or used by, their employees, self-employed persons in respect of work equipment they use and other persons (such as visitors).

7.3.2 Lifting Operations and Lifting Equipment Regulations (LOLER)

LOLER deals with the specific risks arising from the use of work equipment (including lifting accessories) to lift loads. They build upon PUWER and apply to the same groups of people.

LOLER requirements are shown below.

- All lifting operations are planned, supervised and carried out safely.
- Specific requirements are applied to the lifting of people.
- Pre-use checks and inspections at appropriate intervals are carried out on lifting equipment.
- Lifting equipment is thoroughly examined by a competent person on specified occasions and at specified intervals.

Lifting equipment first supplied after 1 January 1995 must be CE marked and meet the essential health and safety requirements of the Supply of Machinery (Safety) Regulations. Consequently, most items of lifting equipment are designed to a harmonised European Standard (such as EN 13000 for mobile cranes, EN 14439 for tower cranes or EN 280 for MEWPs).

For a list of definitions refer to Appendix A.

7.4 Planning of lifting operations

The siting, setting up and use of lifting equipment for lifting operations requires careful planning if all this work is to be carried out safely and efficiently. One person with sufficient training, practical and theoretical knowledge and experience should be appointed to be responsible for planning and supervising the tasks. This person is known as the *competent person* in LOLER or the *appointed person* in BS 7121.

Lifting operations, no matter how large or small, must be properly planned

The competent (appointed) person must ensure that the planning for each task includes the following.

- Identifying the task to be undertaken.
- Identifying the hazards associated with the task.
- Carrying out a risk assessment.
- Identifying control measures.
- Developing the method to be used.
- Recording the planning in a method statement (including any contingency work for rescue).
- Communicating the plan to all persons involved.
- Reviewing the plan before the task starts and incorporating any changing circumstances.

7.4.1 Categorising the lift

To enable lifts to be planned, supervised and carried out effectively, three categories of lift are detailed below. The category into which a particular lift will fall depends on the assessment of the hazards associated with both the environment in which the lift is to be carried out and those associated with the load and lifting equipment.

As shown in the table, increases in either and both environmental or load complexity (the *complexity index*) will lead to the lift being allocated a higher category. Having identified the hazards associated with a particular lift, a hierarchy of control measures should be applied to eliminate or control those hazards.

Environmental complexity (E)		Load complexity (L) 1	Load complexity (L) 2	Load complexity (L) 3
	3	*Complex*	*Complex*	*Complex*
	2	*Intermediate*	*Intermediate*	*Complex*
	1	*Basic*	*Intermediate*	*Complex*

Relationship between complexity index and lift category

The case study in Appendix B shows examples of where the same basic lifting task will fall into different lift categories, depending on differing environmental or load complexities.

7.4.1.1 Basic lift

For a basic lift the duties of the competent (appointed) person should include the following.

- Establishing the complexity of the lifting operation, including load and environmental complexity.
  - Load complexity will include characteristics such as weight, centre of gravity and presence of suitable lifting points. This can be established by a reliable source of information, measuring and weighing the load, or calculation.

    Note: where the weight of the load cannot be accurately established, the notional weight must be multiplied by an appropriate factor (typically 1.5) to allow for possible inaccuracies.
  - Consideration of environmental hazards at the location of the operation will include the access and egress required for the lifting equipment and the suitability of the ground to take the loads imposed by the lifting equipment during preparation for the lift and during the lift itself.
- Selecting the lifting equipment, based on the load characteristics (including weight of the load and any lifting accessories), the maximum height of lift and the maximum radius required. The rated capacity of the lifting equipment should be specified by the manufacturer/installer in the user information supplied with the lifting equipment. In cases where the lifting equipment has been derated at the time of thorough examination, the rated capacity stated on the current report of thorough examination, issued by the competent person, should be used. Manufacturer's sales leaflets and model classifications marked on the machine should not be relied on for the rated capacity of specific lifting equipment.
- Ensuring that the lifting equipment is not operated in wind speeds in excess of those given in the instruction manual for the lifting equipment. The wind area of the load should also be taken into account to ensure that its movement in the wind does not present a hazard.
- Ensuring that the lifting equipment has been thoroughly examined at least within the previous 12 months (or six months for the lifting of persons), inspected and checked before use. It is essential that the report of thorough examination, which confirms that the equipment is safe to use, is available.

  Note: the report of thorough examination for the lifting equipment should be carried with the machine.
- Selecting appropriate lifting accessories, including their method of attachment to the load, configuration and any protection used to prevent damage.
- Ensuring that lifting accessories have been thoroughly examined, at least within the previous six months, inspected and checked before use. It is essential that the report of thorough examination is available to confirm that the lifting accessories are safe to use.

- Ensuring that a system for reporting and rectifying defects is in place.
- Designating a suitable person to check the lifting accessories and any lifting points that are provided on the load to ensure they are free from any obvious defect before attaching the load to the lifting equipment.
- Ensuring that the outcomes of the planning process are recorded in a risk assessment and method statement, which should be signed by the competent (appointed) person.

  Note: *in many instances a basic lift may be covered by a generic risk assessment and a generic method statement, provided that no additional hazards are identified on site.*
- Selecting and defining the roles of the members of the lifting team. In many instances it may be possible to combine some of the roles of members of the lifting team.
- Briefing all persons involved in the lifting operation to ensure that the safe system of work described in the method statement is understood. All persons involved in the lifting operation should be instructed to seek advice from the competent (appointed) person if any change is required to the lifting operation, or if any doubts about safety arise. If one or more handlines/taglines are required to give more control of the load, the competent (appointed) person should designate persons to handle the lines.
- Checking, if numerous loads are to be lifted over a long period, that no changes are required in the safe system of work.
- Ensuring that there is a crane (lift) supervisor designated to direct personnel and that the operation is carried out in accordance with the method statement.

The competent (appointed) person and crane supervisor should be aware of the limits of their knowledge and experience concerning lifting operations and, when conditions exceed these limits, further advice should be sought.

7.4.1.2 Intermediate lift

For an intermediate lift the duties of the competent (appointed) person should include the following, in addition to the duties listed above.

Intermediate lifts were previously called standard lifts in the BS 7121 series – this led to confusion between basic and standard lifts, hence the change from standard to intermediate.

- Identifying all significant hazards in the operating area, including any areas required for access or setting up of the lifting equipment.

  Note: *this may involve the competent (appointed) person visiting site if there are any concerns about the detail and quality of the information with which the competent (appointed) person has been provided.*
- Ensuring that a site/task-specific risk assessment and method statement, detailing control measures for the identified risks, is prepared.
- Liaising with any other person or authority, as required, to overcome any hazard, by including any necessary corrective action or special measures in the safe system of work.
- Determining any requirement for personnel in addition to the lifting equipment operator (such as a slinger, signaller or dedicated crane (lift) supervisor).
- Considering the effect of the lifting operation on surrounding property or persons, including the general public. This should lead to arranging for appropriate action to minimise any adverse effects, and to giving appropriate notice to all persons concerned.

7.4.1.3 Complex lift

For a complex lift the duties of the competent (appointed) person should include the following, in addition to the duties listed for basic and intermediate lifts.

- Identifying all exceptional hazards in the operating area, including any areas required for access or setting up of the lifting equipment. This will require the competent (appointed) person to visit the location of the planned lifting operation as part of the planning process.
- Liaising with any other person or authority, as required to overcome any hazard, by including any necessary corrective action or special measures in the safe system of work.
- Ensuring that the method statement includes the exact sequence of operations when lifting the load.
- Preparing a sufficiently detailed and dimensioned drawing of the site, lifting equipment and the load, identifying the load path, pick up and set down areas, together with the position of any exceptional hazards in the area. The information provided should be sufficient to enable the operator to position the lifting equipment accurately.

It is good practice for the competent (appointed) person to be present on the site during a complex lift.

Complexity of a lift

The case study in Appendix B illustrates the way in which both the complexity of the load being lifted and the environment in which the lift is taking place affect the overall complexity of the lift. The case study takes a typical construction lifting operation; the lifting of a generator and fuel tank. Three different situations are evaluated with examples of the hazards encountered and the control measures required to eliminate or reduce those hazards to an acceptable level. It should be noted that this is an example only and does not identify all the hazards that may be present in a given circumstance.

7.4.2 Identifying the task to be undertaken

As the first stage in the planning process, the task to be undertaken should be clearly identified, together with the location and sequence.

Certain lifting operations require particular care and attention. Further advice can be found in BS 7121 Part 1. The competent (appointed) person should be familiar with these and plan the lift accordingly.

7.4.3 Surveying the site

The planning of a lift using lifting equipment may involve a site survey, carried out by the competent (appointed) person or their representative. This involves visiting the location where the task is to be carried out so that both the task and any hazards involved can be identified. For simple tasks the remainder of the planning process may be completed at the same time, whilst for more complicated jobs the person carrying out the survey may need to complete the process off site. The survey should include assessment of ground conditions.

A further site visit may be required prior to the lifting operation being executed to ensure no changes have been made to the environment.

7.4.4 Identifying the hazards associated with the task

The hazards associated with the task should be identified. These might be associated with the location where the work is to be carried out, the nature of the lifting equipment, the load to be lifted or the people associated with the task or located in the vicinity.

7.4.5 Carrying out a risk assessment

Having identified the hazards associated with the task, a risk assessment should be carried out to identify who might be harmed, the chance of them being harmed and the consequences of any harm. This assessment should be recorded.

7.4.6 Identifying control measures

Once the risk assessment has highlighted the risks involved in the task, the procedures and measures required to control them should be identified.

7.4.7 Developing the method to be used

Having identified the hazards, evaluated the risks and worked out the control measures required to carry out the task safely, these components should be developed into a coherent plan. Any contingency measures and rescue procedures should be included in the plan.

7.4.8 Selecting lifting equipment and lifting accessories

A proprietary manhole lifting attachment

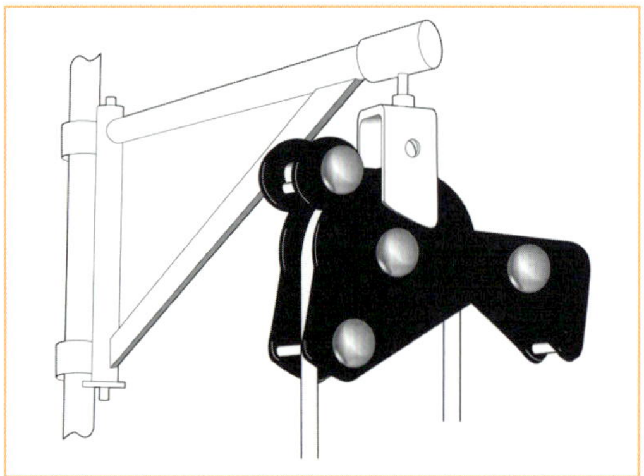

Inertia braked gin wheels are now common practice and far safer than traditional gin wheels

LOLER requires that lifting equipment and lifting accessories are of adequate strength and stability for the load being lifted. Consider the following when selecting lifting equipment and lifting accessories for a particular task.

- Weight, dimensions and characteristics of the loader and the loads to be lifted.
- Operation, speed, radii, height of lift and areas of movement.
- Number, frequency and types of lifting operation.
- Space available for lifting equipment access, deployment, operation and stowage, including the space required for correct deployment of stabilisers.
- Control position that will be most suitable for the lifting operation (the control position should be selected to ensure that the operator has an adequate view of the load path and is adequately protected from crushing hazards).
- Need for motion-limiting devices (such as slewing arc or height limiters).
- Effect of the operating environment on the lifting equipment.

7.4.9 Recording the planning in a method statement

Once the plan has been developed it should be recorded in a method statement. The length and detail of this document depends on the complexity of the task to be undertaken and on the risks involved. A simple, low risk job (such as a routine delivery and unloading of bulk materials or blocks to site) might only require the use of a brief, generic method statement, whilst a more complex and high risk job (such as delivering, unloading, and assembling and lifting into position a loading platform on a construction site) would require a more detailed job specific method statement. The method statement covering all planned lifting on a site is often referred to as the lift plan.

Telehandlers should have, and follow, a lifting plan

The method statement should include a lifting schedule, listing each type of item to be lifted together with the following information.

- Item description.
- Weight.
- Dimensions.
- Lifting points and method.
- Type of lifting accessories to be used and configuration.
- Pick up and landing locations referenced to the site plan.

For an example of a lift plan and lift schedule refer to Section G: *Checklists and forms*.

7.4.10 Communicating the plan to all persons involved

One of the most important aspects of successful planning is to ensure that the contents of the plan are communicated effectively to and between all parties involved, taking account of language differences. Arrangements should be made to ensure that copies of any method statements are given to the appropriate people and that others involved in the job are fully briefed. Similarly, any changes to the plan should be communicated to all parties.

7.4.11 Reviewing the plan before the job starts

Immediately before a job starts, the risk assessment and method statement should be reviewed to check if any aspects of the job have changed and the effect that these changes could have on the safety of the operation. If any modifications to the plan are required these should be communicated to all those involved. The competent (appointed) person should amend the method statement (lift plan) and initial any significant changes.

For further guidance on planning of lifting and installation refer to:

- ***Code of Practice for safe use of cranes – Part 1 General and Part 3 Mobile cranes* (BS 7121)**
- ***Safe use of lifting equipment – Lifting Operations and Lifting Equipment Regulations 1998* Code of Practice (L113)**
- **HSE leaflet *Five steps to risk assessment* (INDG163)**
- **CIRIA publication *Crane stability on site* (C703).**

7.5 Control of lifting operations

When a lifting operation is undertaken it is essential that it is adequately controlled by suitably trained and competent people. Depending on the complexity of the lift the following roles may be involved.

- ☑ **Competent (appointed) person.** Although the competent (appointed) person has overall responsibility for the lift, they may choose to supervise the operation themselves or delegate the role to a crane (lift) supervisor.
- ☑ **Crane (lift) supervisor** supervises the lifting operation on behalf of the competent (appointed) person, working to the approved method statement or lift plan. If circumstances require any change to the method statement, this must be approved by the competent (appointed) person.
- ☑ **Operator** operates the lifting equipment within its permitted duties in accordance with the method statement and as instructed by the crane (lift) supervisor.
- ☑ **Slinger/signaller** connects lifting accessories to the load, initiates lifting by signalling to the operator, observes the path of the load to its destination, signals to the operator and detaches lifting accessories once the load is safely landed.

7.5.1 Combination of roles

In certain circumstances it may be possible to combine some of the roles of members of the lifting team (illustrated in the table below). However, the table should not be taken as definitive for every circumstance. Role combination should only take place following review of the lifting operation by the competent (appointed) person.

It should be noted that a competent (appointed) person is required to plan all lifting operations. It is good practice for them to be present on the site during a complex lift.

In some circumstances it may be appropriate for the competent (appointed) person to also assume other roles (such as crane supervisor, slinger/signaller or operator).

The combination of roles requires that the person undertaking the combined role has achieved the necessary competence for each role.

<table>
<tr><th rowspan="2">Activity</th><th rowspan="2">Role</th><th colspan="3">Lift category</th></tr>
<tr><th>Basic</th><th>Intermediate</th><th>Complex</th></tr>
<tr><td>Planning</td><td>Competent (appointed) person</td><td>Required</td><td>Required</td><td>Required</td></tr>
<tr><td>Site visit</td><td>Competent (appointed) person</td><td>Not essential</td><td>May be required</td><td>Required</td></tr>
<tr><td rowspan="4">Lifting operation</td><td>Competent (appointed) person</td><td>Not essential</td><td>May be required</td><td>Required</td></tr>
<tr><td>Crane (lift) supervisor</td><td rowspan="3">Roles may be combined</td><td rowspan="2">Roles may be combined</td><td>Required</td></tr>
<tr><td>Operator</td><td>Required</td></tr>
<tr><td>Slinger/signaller</td><td>Required</td><td>Required</td></tr>
<tr><td colspan="5">Note: this table is for guidance. It is the competent (appointed) person's responsibility to determine the combination of roles for each lifting operation following a site-specific risk assessment that takes account of the load, the lifting equipment and the site environment.</td></tr>
</table>

7.5.2 Signalling methods

Communication between the various people involved in the lifting operation should be clear and unambiguous. This can be by recognised hand signals *(refer to Appendix C)* or voice communication using portable radios. Slinger/signallers should be provided with distinctive personal protective equipment (PPE) (such as fluorescent hard-hat covers) so that they are immediately identifiable to the lifting equipment operator.

www.

For further information on radio communications for lifting operations refer to the Construction Plant-hire Association's Technical information note 017.

7.6 Training and competence of personnel

It is essential that all personnel involved in the planning, supervision and carrying out of lifting operations are competent for their role. There are a number of nationally recognised card schemes that provide evidence of training and, in the case of the Construction Plant Competence Scheme (CPCS), competence. It is, however, the responsibility of each employer to ensure that their employees and those working under their control, are competent to undertake the tasks they have been allocated.

It is also important that lifting equipment operators are familiar with the specific machine they are operating. Lifting equipment comes in many shapes and sizes, with significant differences in control layouts and operating characteristics. It is therefore essential that operators are given adequate familiarisation on an unfamiliar type or model of machine before they begin lifting operations. This is generally carried out by an experienced person employed by the lifting equipment owner.

For further guidance on training and competence refer to BS 7121 Parts 1, 3, 4 and 5.

7.6.1 Medical fitness

People who operate plant have the potential to injure both themselves and other people in the workplace and the surrounding area. Ensuring that construction plant operators are medically fit to operate is primarily an issue for their employers, who have a duty to ensure that any employee is physically and mentally capable of undertaking the tasks they are required to carry out. Others in the construction sector (such as the principal contractor and sub-contractors) will also have an interest in ensuring that plant operators have an appropriate level of fitness.

For detailed guidance on medical fitness refer to the Strategic Forum for Construction Plant Safety Group's *Medical fitness to operate construction plant* (Good practice guide).

7.7 Lifting persons

Some items of lifting equipment (such as mobile elevating work platforms (MEWPs) or suspended cradles) are specifically designed for the lifting of persons and this type of equipment should be used wherever possible.

Signaller directing the lift of a man riding cage

The Approved Code of Practice to Regulation 5 of LOLER says: 'The raising and lowering of people by work equipment, which is not specifically designed for the purpose, should only be undertaken in exceptional circumstances, when it is not practicable to gain access by less hazardous means. Where it is necessary to use such work equipment then you should ensure that all necessary precautions are taken to ensure safety, including appropriate supervision'.

If people are being lifted by lifting equipment not specifically designed for the purpose, steps must be taken to ensure the following.

- ✓ The carrier is constructed to prevent a person using it from being crushed, trapped or falling from the carrier, either during lifting or carrying out work from the carrier.
- ✓ Fall protection PPE is worn.
- ✓ The equipment is equipped with suitable devices to prevent the carrier falling.
- ✓ A person trapped in a carrier is not exposed to danger and can be rescued in the event of the lifting equipment breaking down.

For further guidance on MEWPs refer to Chapter C08 Lifting equipment.

If a person-riding basket or carrier suspended from a crane is being used, BS 7172 Part 1 Clause 23 gives detailed advice.

C
07

7.8 Siting of lifting equipment

For further detailed guidance on the siting of lifting equipment refer to:

- ☑ ***Code of Practice for safe use of cranes – Parts 1, 3, 4 and 5*** **(BS 7121)**
- ☑ ***Code of Practice for the safe use of construction hoists*** **(BS 7212)**
- ☑ ***Code of Practice for the safe use of mast climbing work platforms*** **(BS 7981)**
- ☑ ***Code of Practice for the safe use of mobile elevating work platforms*** **(BS 8460)**
- ☑ **CIRIA publication** ***Crane stability on site*** **(C703).**

The area where lifting equipment is to be sited must be carefully assessed to ensure that it is suitable before the equipment is taken to site and put into service. During this assessment, the following points should be considered.

7.8.1 Clearances

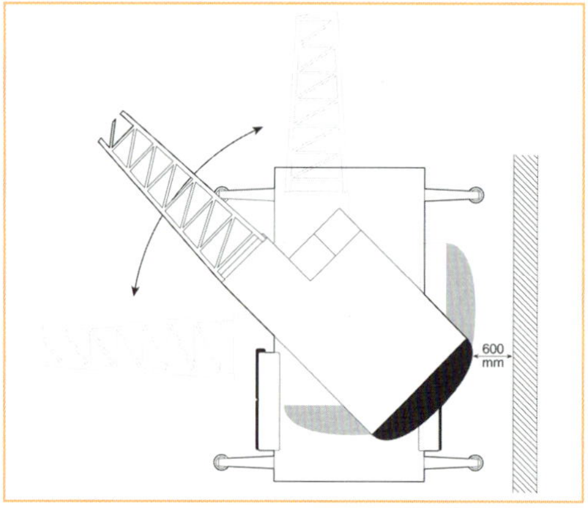

The area chosen must be of a sufficient size to enable the lifting equipment to be manoeuvred into position, set up or installed, operated and stowed, with sufficient clearances between the lifting equipment and surrounding structures, as detailed in the manufacturer's operation and instruction manual. This is to ensure that trapping points are not created and that damage does not occur to either the lifting equipment or the surrounding structures. A gap into which persons may enter, which may be reduced by a slewing motion, should be at least 0.5 m, but preferably never less than 0.6 m.

7.8.2 Ground conditions

Insufficient consideration and assessment of ground conditions has been found to be a major cause of accidents with lifting equipment.

The stability of most mobile lifting equipment relies on the ground on which it stands being able to safely absorb the loads imposed by the machine. Most lifting equipment manufacturers supply information on the loads imposed by the machine on the ground in the various operating and set-up configurations of the equipment. These generally consist of the following.

- ☑ Maximum vertical load per stabiliser (or wheel for free-on-wheels machines).
- ☑ Dimensions of stabiliser support plate (pad).
- ☑ Ground-level pressure on stabiliser support plate.

An assessment of the ability of the ground to accept these loads should be made by a competent person.

This assessment may indicate that the ground has insufficient bearing capacity to accept the loads imposed by the lifting equipment, in which case additional measures will need to be taken before the equipment can be set up. These may include using timber sleepers, proprietary mats or, in extreme cases, concrete pads to spread the applied load to an acceptable bearing pressure.

Where timber is to be used it is important that the timber sections employed are of sufficient dimensions and strength to transmit the applied loads to the ground and that the timbers are pinned together to form a grillage. The use of individual loose timbers has been found to be a major cause of accidents.

It is essential that any stabilisers are deployed in the manner specified by the lifting equipment manufacturer.

When siting the lifting equipment, consideration should be given to the length of time that the equipment will be erected in one position and the likely deterioration of the supporting ground or foundation over time (such as timber rotting, undermining by water or frost, drying out and adjacent excavations).

Below are some of the hazards that need to be considered when assessing the ground.

- Underground services.
- Paved areas.
- Uncompacted fill.
- Open excavations.
- High water table.
- Basements.
- Cellars.
- Proximity to canals and rivers.
- Changes to site conditions during construction.
- Slope and camber of ground.

Details of any foundation or load spreading arrangements should be recorded in the method statement by the competent (appointed) person.

For further guidance on assessment of ground conditions and lifting equipment foundations refer to the CIRIA publications:

- ***Crane stability on site* (C703)**
- ***Tower crane stability* (C654).**

7.8.3 Overhead hazards

When siting lifting equipment care must be taken to ensure that the extending structure will not contact or approach overhead hazards (such as power lines, communications cables or overhead structures).

Pre-planning of safe working procedures is important. The first step in avoiding danger is to find out whether there is an overhead electric line within or immediately adjoining the work area, or across any route to it.

Information may be available from the local electricity supplier about the location of their lines.

If any such lines are found it should be assumed that they are live unless or until this has been proved otherwise by their owners.

If there are any electric power lines over the work area, near the site boundaries, or over access roads to the work area, consult the owners of the lines so that the proposed plan of work can be discussed. Allow sufficient time for the line to be diverted or made dead, or for other precautions to be taken, as described below.

If the lines can only be made dead for short periods, then the passage of tall plant and, as far as is possible, other work around the lines should be scheduled at these times.

Liaison between the persons responsible for the work and the owner(s) of the lines should be continued until the work has been completed.

For further advice on siting and use of lifting equipment near to overhead power lines refer to the Health and Safety Executive's *Avoidance of danger from overhead electric power lines* (Guidance note GS6) and the Energy Networks Associations' *The safe use of mechanical plant in the vicinity of electricity overhead lines*.

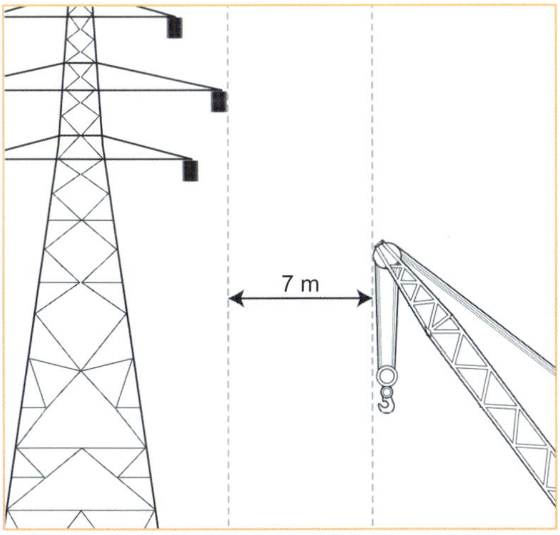

As a guide, the minimum safe working distance between the lifting equipment (usually the tip of the jib) and the power cable is:

- 3 m if the cables are suspended on wooden poles
- 7 m if the cables are suspended on metal pylons.

Both measurements should be taken from a point on the ground directly below the outermost cable to the tip of the jib when it is nearest to the cable.

7.8.4 Noise

Some locations where lifting equipment is used may have restrictions on noise, particularly at night, and the competent (appointed) person should ensure that any such restrictions are taken into account in the planning process.

7.8.5 Exhaust gas emissions

If lifting equipment powered by an internal combustion engine is to be used in a confined space the competent (appointed) person should consider the effect of vehicle exhaust gas emissions on persons in the vicinity and take appropriate measures (such as forced ventilation or the use of fume extraction ducts).

7.8.6 Proximity to railways and airports

If the lifting equipment is to be sited adjacent to a railway or in the vicinity of an airfield or airport, the competent (appointed) person should contact the operator of the railway or airport as they may well impose restrictions on the height, lifting capacity and use of the lifting equipment.

The competent (appointed) person should consult the aerodrome/airfield manager for permission to work if a crane is to be used within 6 km of the aerodrome/airfield and its height exceeds 10 m or that of the surrounding structures or trees.

The Air Navigation Order makes it an offence to act recklessly or negligently in a manner likely to endanger aircraft.

Further guidance on the use of lifting equipment in the vicinity of airfields is given in the following publications.

- ***Operating tower cranes in the vicinity of aerodromes, notification and en-route obstacle lighting* (Technical information note 039). Construction Plant-hire Association.**
- ***Guidance to crane operators on aviation lighting and notification*. Civil Aviation Authority.**
- ***A voluntary Code of Practice for the safe use of cranes in and around airports*. Off-highway Plant and Equipment Research Centre.**

7.8.7 Access and egress to and from the site

It is important when siting lifting equipment to ensure that there is adequate access to the set-up position for both the machine and any supporting transport. It is equally important to ensure that adequate egress will be available when the lifting equipment is removed from site.

A self-erecting tower crane

A self-erecting tower crane was being used for lifting on a refurbishment project in a town centre. The crane stood in a courtyard for the duration of the project and the only way into the courtyard was through a single archway, which was just high enough to allow the folded self-erecting tower crane to pass below. During construction a beam was inserted at the top of the arch to support a wall being constructed above. When it was time to remove the crane from site it was found that the headroom had been reduced to such an extent that the crane could not pass through the archway. The only way to remove the crane was to dismantle it at considerable cost and inconvenience to the site.

7.8.8 Wind

The lifting equipment supplier or manufacturer will be able to advise on the maximum in-service and out-of-service wind conditions for the specific model of lifting equipment to be used. It should be borne in mind that this is a design maximum wind speed and the operator may decide to take the crane out of service at a lower speed due to the type of load being lifted or difficulty in controlling the crane. **The operator has the primary responsibility for making the decision, in conjunction with the appointed person or crane supervisor.**

The operator's decision to take the crane out of service should not be overridden by site management under any circumstances.

The wind forces exerted on both an item of lifting equipment and any load suspended from it may be quite large and affect both the strength and stability of the lifting equipment, and safe handling of the load. It is not always appreciated that these forces are due to wind pressure, not wind speed, and consequently, if the wind speed doubles, the wind pressure increases by a factor of four. This means that a small increase in wind speed can have a significant effect on the safe operation of the lifting equipment.

Wind speeds should be monitored by either the anemometer installed on the lifting equipment (such as tower cranes and large mobile cranes and MEWPs) or the use of hand-held anemometers, bearing in mind that wind speed increases with height and that the wind pressure on the load may increase as it is lifted. All operating personnel should be aware of the maximum in-service wind speed for the particular lifting equipment being used. This value may need to be significantly reduced when lifting loads with a large wind sail area.

Tower cranes normally have a maximum in-service design wind speed of 45 mph (20 m/s, 72 kph), but following a review of in-service wind speeds by the CPA Tower Crane Interest Group, involving tower crane suppliers, major contractors and the Health and Safety Executive (HSE), the industry-recommended maximum wind speed at which tower cranes operating in the UK must be taken out of service is 38 mph (16.5 m/s, 60 kph). This takes into account the time required to take the crane out of service and the difficulty of lifting large area loads in high winds.

For mobile cranes, the duty charts will specify the maximum wind speed at which the mobile crane must be taken out of service. This value will vary with the specific make and model of crane and also the duty on which it is rigged, but normally has a maximum value of 31 mph (14 m/s, 50 kph) and is frequently below this value.

For further information on wind speeds and how they may be estimated by use of the Beaufort scale, refer to Appendix E.

For specific guidance on the effect of loads with large wind sail areas on limiting wind speeds, refer to the Liebherr publication *Influence of wind on crane operations* which can be downloaded from its website free of charge.

7.8.9 Radio communication systems

Lifting equipment often works on congested construction sites where the signaller is out of sight of the lifting equipment operator (blind lifts) and the standard hand signals specified in BS 7121 cannot be used. As an alternative, hand-held VHF/UHF radios are often used. This, however, can lead to a number of problems that may interfere with the clear communication vital for safe lifting operations. Some examples are shown below.

Signaller making radio contact with crane operator

- Loss of signal and thus communication, leading to loss of control of the lifting operation.
- Interference from radios on adjacent sites, which can lead to loss of communication or directions to the lifting equipment operator.
- A misunderstanding between the lifting equipment operator and the signaller, leading to problems, such as a load being lifted before the slinger has their hands clear, loads colliding with a building and the load being lowered before people are clear of the landing area.

If communication is lost during a lifting operation, the operator must stop immediately until communication is regained.

7.9 Operation of lifting equipment

Lifting equipment should be operated by operators who have been trained and assessed as competent.

7.9.1 Manuals and signs

All operations should be carried out in accordance with the manufacturer's operating instruction manual, a copy of which should be with the lifting equipment at all times. Checks should be made by the supplier to ensure that the manual is the correct manual for the lifting equipment supplied, conveys information to the users in a simple and understandable format and is in a language (normally English) that is readily understood by the operator.

All signs, labels and decals on the lifting equipment must be clear, legible and in a language (normally English) that is readily understood by the operator. A rated capacity chart for the specific lifting equipment must be readily available to the operator.

7.9.2 Pedestrian operated lifting equipment

The operation of some types of lifting equipment (such as lorry loaders and self-erecting tower cranes) is frequently carried out by a pedestrian operator at ground level, using remote controls that may be pendant controlled or use a wireless data transmission system. Whilst pedestrian control provides flexibility with the possible combination of roles there are several potential disadvantages that must be taken into account in planning the lifting operations. Operators may:

- ☑ be at risk of tripping and falling when trying to move around the site over uneven ground whilst concentrating on controlling the lifting equipment or handling the load (pedestrian operated lifting equipment should only be controlled whilst the operator is stationary)
- ☑ not have a good view of the load and any obstructions and consequently must always have the lifting equipment jib or boom and load in sight at all times, unless they are working under the direction of a signaller who has a clear view of the load and load path
- ☑ put themselves in a hazardous position, where they may be struck by the load or part of the lifting equipment.

! Operating lifting equipment with remote controls

Operators should always:

- ☑ check site rules to confirm that the use of a remote control is permitted
- ☑ use the belt/neck strap provided
- ☑ be aware of the working area, including their proximity to the load and vehicle
- ☑ use in accordance with the manufacturer's instructions
- ☑ ensure the remote is deactivated when not in use
- ☑ store the control unit in a suitable place when not in use

and should never:

- ☒ stand between the load and a fixed object (such as the vehicle or a wall)
- ☒ walk whilst operating the remote control.

C 07

7.9.3 Radio remote controls

To prevent unauthorised use, the operator of lifting equipment that is controlled by transmitted signals (such as radio signals) should retain the control station (transmitter) in their physical possession or remove the key from its key-lock switch and, for short periods, retain the key in their possession. For longer periods, or when the lifting equipment is not in use, the transmitter should be kept in secure storage.

When the transmitter is fitted with a belt or harness, the operator should be wearing the harness before switching on the transmitter so that accidental operation of the lifting equipment is prevented. The transmitter should only be switched on when operating the lifting equipment and should be switched off before removing the harness and when attaching loads.

7.9.4 Rated capacity

The rated capacity (safe working load) of lifting equipment should not be exceeded, except when testing the lifting equipment under the supervision of a competent person.

Care should be taken to prevent pendulum swinging of the load by careful control of the operating motions to match the swing of the load and to keep it under control at all times.

Rated capacities apply only to freely suspended loads. The hoisting, slewing, telescoping, or raising and lowering motions of lifting equipment should not be used to drag a load under any circumstances. Before lifting a load, the hook and hoist rope should be vertically above the centre of gravity of the load. Failure to observe these points can adversely affect the stability of the lifting equipment or introduce loadings (stresses) into the lifting equipment structure for which it has not been designed and, even with a rated capacity indicator/limiter fitted, a sudden structural failure or overturn can occur without warning.

It is essential that all lifting equipment is clearly marked to indicate its rated capacity. Where the rated capacity depends on the lifting equipment's configuration (such as changing radius) it shall be clearly marked to indicate its rated capacity for each configuration. As an alternative, information that clearly indicates its rated capacity for each configuration should be kept with the lifting equipment.

Lifting equipment designed for lifting persons should be clearly marked to indicate that it is equipment for lifting persons, whilst lifting equipment not designed for lifting persons, but which might be used in error, must be clearly marked to indicate that it is not designed for lifting persons.

Most lifting equipment with a rated capacity not less than 1,000 kg or an overturning moment not less than 40,000 Nm is fitted with a load control device that will sense when the rated capacity has been exceeded and prevent further movement. These devices vary between different types of lifting equipment and on cranes are generally known as rated capacity limiters (RCL). Cranes are also fitted with rated capacity indicators (RCI), which indicate approach to overload and overload.

Effective lift planning should ensure that the rated capacity of lifting equipment is never exceeded. The RCL or load control device should never be used to establish the weight of a load.

7.9.5 Handling of loads near persons

When loads have to be handled in the vicinity of persons, extreme care should be exercised and adequate clearances allowed. The route of the load should be planned to prevent lifting over persons. Operators and signallers should pay particular attention to possible dangers of persons working out of sight.

All persons should be instructed to stand clear of the load being lifted. When lifting from a stack, all persons should be instructed to stand away from the stack in case adjacent materials or objects are displaced. This also applies to the removal of part loads from the deck of a vehicle.

Where possible, lifting of loads over highways, railways, rivers, or other places to which the public have access, should be avoided. If this is not possible, permission should be obtained from the appropriate authority and the area kept clear of traffic and persons.

7.9.6 Multiple lifting

Multiple or tandem lifting (carrying out a lift with more than one piece of lifting equipment attached to the load) should always be planned and carried out with great care. A multiple lift is always classified as complex. Multiple lifts are generally only carried out with mobile cranes. Consequently the term *crane* will be used here, rather than lifting equipment.

7.9.6.1 Weight of the load

The total weight of the load and its distribution should be either known or calculated. Where the information is taken from a drawing, due allowance should be made for manufacturing tolerances.

7.9.6.2 Centre of gravity

Owing to the variable effect of manufacturing tolerances, variable density, and so on, the centre of gravity of the load might not be known accurately and the proportion of the load being carried by each machine could therefore be uncertain.

7.9.6.3 Weight of the lifting accessories/attachments

The weight of the lifting accessories/attachments should be part of the calculated load on the cranes. When handling heavy or awkwardly shaped loads, the deduction from the rated capacity of the lifting equipment to allow for the weight of the lifting accessories/attachments might be significant. The weight of the lifting accessories/attachments, and hook blocks, where appropriate, and its distribution should therefore be accurately known.

In cases where the hoist ropes are reeved around pulleys that are part of a specially designed lifting accessory/attachment (such as a lifting beam) the weight of the removed hook block and hook may be taken into consideration when determining the net weight of the lifting accessories/attachments.

7.9.6.4 Capacities of the lifting accessories/attachments

The distribution of the forces within the lifting accessories or attachments, that arise during the lifting operation, should be established. The lifting accessories/attachments used should, unless specially designed for the particular lifting operation, have a capacity margin well in excess of that needed for its proportioned load.

Special lifting accessories/attachments might be necessary to suit the maximum variation in distribution and direction of application of loads or forces that can occur during multiple lifting.

7.9.6.5 Synchronisation of lifting equipment motions

If the variations in the direction and magnitude of the forces acting on the crane during the multiple lift are to be kept to a minimum, it is essential that the crane motions are synchronised.

Lifting equipment/cranes of equal capacity and similar characteristics should therefore be used whenever possible. In practice, there is always some variation due to differences in response to the activation of the control system.

The rated capacity of a crane is calculated on the assumption that the load is raised and lowered in a vertical plane. The crane structure is designed to withstand any lateral loads imposed by accelerations in the various crane motions, but it is unsafe to rely on this lateral strength to withstand horizontal components of 'out-of-vertical' lifts.

If the cranes have dissimilar characteristics, it is unlikely that the motions will be accurately synchronised. Therefore, an assessment should be made of the effect of variation in verticality of the hoist ropes that could arise from inequalities of speed, together with a determination of the means for keeping such inequalities to a minimum.

7.9.6.6 Instrumentation

Instruments are available to monitor the angle of the load and verticality and the force in any hoist rope constantly throughout the lifting operation. The use of such instruments and the restriction of the motion speeds, together with the strict use of one motion at any one time, can assist in the control of the loads on the cranes within the planned values.

7.9.6.7 Supervision

One competent person should be in attendance and in overall control of a multiple crane operation. Only this person should give instructions to personnel operating or driving machines, except in an emergency when a commonly recognised stop signal may be given by any person observing a situation leading to danger.

If all the necessary points cannot be observed from one position, other personnel should be positioned at various points to observe and report to the person in charge of the operation.

It is essential that adequate means of signalling are provided between the person in charge of the operation, the operators of the cranes, and the slingers and signallers.

7.9.6.8 Recommended rated capacity during lifting

As all the factors cannot be accurately evaluated, an appropriate down-rating should be applied to all the cranes involved. The down-rating might need to be 20% or more.

7.10 Maintenance, checks and inspections

Maintenance, checks and inspections of lifting equipment are essential if it is not to deteriorate over time, break down and ultimately fail. All maintenance should be carried out by a competent person who is familiar with the equipment and has the knowledge and experience to detect and repair existing or potential faults. The maintenance should be in accordance with the manufacturer's instructions and carried out at the recommended intervals.

All lifting equipment should have a pre-use check carried out daily or at the start of each shift and any defects reported to a supervisor. This is normally undertaken by the operator who should be trained to carry out the checks.

In addition to pre-use checks, inspections should be carried out at appropriate intervals, either as part of the maintenance process or at more frequent intervals (such as the weekly inspection of mobile cranes). The frequency of inspections will depend on assessment of the risk of failure of the lifting equipment and should be guided by the manufacturer's instructions.

It is particularly important to ensure at frequent intervals that the load control device or RCL on lifting equipment is functioning correctly.

The results of all checks and inspections should be recorded and there should be a system in place to ensure that all reported defects are rectified and recorded.

Each item of lifting equipment should have a history file containing all records of maintenance, inspection and through examination, so that maintenance trends can be established and adequate maintenance demonstrated in the event of an accident.

For further guidance on maintenance and inspection refer to BS 7121 Parts 2-1, 2-3, 2-4 and 2-5.

7.11 Thorough examination

7.11.1 Types of thorough examination

There are four situations where thorough examination is required by LOLER.

- Before being put into use for the first time.
- After installation on a new site, installation in a new location on the same site or where significant changes have been made to the lifting equipment (such as an extension of a tower crane jib).
- Periodically while in service.
- After exceptional circumstances have occurred.

A thorough examination before first use is not required for new lifting equipment where the user has received an EC declaration of conformity that was made not more than 12 months before the lifting equipment is first put into service.

7.11.2 Frequency

LOLER place a duty on employers to ensure that all lifting equipment and lifting accessories are subjected to a schedule of thorough examinations by a competent person at intervals **not exceeding** six months for lifting equipment used for lifting persons and all lifting accessories, and 12 months for other lifting equipment.

The competent person carrying out the thorough examination may, however, decide, for a variety of reasons, that a schedule of more frequent examinations is appropriate.

A thorough examination must also be carried out after any other event (such as damage or overloading) likely to have affected the safety of any lifting equipment or accessories or where the equipment has been out of use for a long period.

Furthermore, where the safety of lifting equipment depends upon the way it has been installed, as for the many items of temporary lifting equipment used on construction sites (such as hoists and tower cranes) it must be thoroughly examined after assembly and before being put into service at a new site, or a new location on the same site, or after alteration on the same site.

7.11.3 Competent person

The competent person carrying out thorough examinations must have sufficient practical and theoretical knowledge and experience of the lifting equipment to enable defects and weaknesses to be detected, and their importance in relation to the safety of the equipment to be assessed.

It is essential that the competent person is sufficiently independent and impartial to allow objective decisions to be made. This does not mean that competent persons must necessarily be employed from an external company. If employers and others within their own organisations have the necessary competence then they can use it. However, if they do, they must ensure that their in-house examiners have the genuine authority and independence to ensure that examinations are properly carried out and that the necessary recommendations arising from them are made objectively. This means that thorough examinations of lifting equipment should not be carried out by the person carrying out maintenance or installation of that lifting equipment. In practice, lifting equipment where the consequence of failure is greatest (such as tower cranes, mobile cranes, MEWPs and hoists) are generally thoroughly examined by a third party.

C
07

7.11.4 Reporting

Once a thorough examination has been completed the competent person must complete the following.

- Immediately inform both the user and the owner of the lifting equipment of any defect in the lifting equipment, which in their opinion is, or could become, a danger to persons.
- As soon as is practicable make a report of the thorough examination in writing to both the user and the owner of the lifting equipment.
- Where there is, in their opinion, a defect in the lifting equipment involving an existing or imminent risk of serious personal injury, send a copy of the report as soon as is practicable to the relevant enforcing authority (generally the HSE for construction activities).

Reports of thorough examinations must contain the information contained in Schedule 1 of LOLER, which is reproduced in Appendix D.

7.11.5 Retention of reports

LOLER requires that reports of thorough examination are kept for minimum specified periods, depending on the type of thorough examination, as shown in the table below.

Type of equipment	Type of thorough examination	Retention period
Lifting equipment	Before first use	Until the user ceases to use the equipment
Lifting accessories	Before first use	Two years after the report is made
Lifting equipment	After installation at a new site	Until the equipment is removed from site
Lifting equipment and lifting accessories	Periodic	Until the next periodic thorough examination report is made or the expiration of two years, whichever is later
Lifting equipment and lifting accessories	Intermediate inspections	Until the next report is made

Each item of lifting equipment should have a history file containing all records of maintenance, inspection and thorough examination, so that maintenance trends can be established and adequate maintenance demonstrated in the event of an accident.

7.11.6 Testing

LOLER specifies that testing, including overload testing, is part of thorough examination and is carried out at the discretion of the competent person.

The design of some lifting equipment and the use of high tensile materials mean that damage may be caused by conventional overload tests. Consequently, it is important that the competent person carrying out the thorough examination or testing takes account of the manufacturer's instructions and, if necessary, consults the manufacturer before starting testing.

Overload testing is not mandatory and is only carried out when required by the competent person.

For further guidance on thorough examination refer to BS 7121 Parts 2-1, 2-3, 2-4 and 2-5.

Appendix A – Definitions

Competent (appointed) person. A person who has the competence, adequate training, authority and experience to take overall responsibility and control of a lifting operation, having been formally appointed in writing by the management of the organisation(s) that requires the load to be moved.

Competent person. (For the purposes of inspection and examination). A person who has the practical and theoretical knowledge, together with actual experience of what they are to examine, so as to enable them to detect errors, defects, faults or weaknesses, which it is the purpose of the examination or inspection to discover; and to assess the importance of any such discovery.

Crane co-ordinator. A person who plans and directs the sequence of operations of cranes to ensure that they do not collide with other cranes, loads and other equipment (for example, concrete placing booms, telehandlers and piling rigs).

Crane (lift) supervisor. A person who controls the lifting operation and ensures that it is carried out in accordance with the appointed person's safe system of work.

Crane operator. A person who operates the crane for the purpose of moving and positioning loads or erection of the crane.

Lifting accessory. A lifting beam or frame, chain sling, rope sling or similar gear, a ring, link, hook, interlocks, plate clamp, shackle, swivel or eyebolt, and any loose equipment that is used with lifting gear.

Lifting equipment. A piece of work equipment for lifting or lowering loads, including a crab, winch, pulley block or gin wheel (for raising or lowering), a hoist, crane, shearlegs, excavator, dragline, piling frame, aerial cable way, aerial ropeway or overhead runway, goods hoist, MEWP, scissor lift, vehicle hoist, ropes used for access, forklift truck, lorry loader and passenger lift.

Mobile crane. A crane capable of travelling under its own power, but does not include cranes that travel on a line of rails.

Plant and equipment. Any plant, equipment, gear, machinery, apparatus or appliance, or part thereof.

Rated capacity. The load that any item of lifting equipment (such as a crane or hoist), or any accessory for lifting is designed to lift for a given operating condition (such as configuration or position of load). Rated capacity was formerly known as safe working load (SWL).

On certain types of crane (for example, mobile cranes), the rated capacity includes the weight of the hook block and all the lifting gear. The weight of these should be deducted from the declared rated capacity of the lifting equipment to obtain the net load that can be safely lifted.

Rated capacity indicator/limiter RCI/L. Device(s) that warns of the approach to overload and prevents the crane from being overloaded as described in BS EN 12077-2.

Thorough examination. An examination by a competent person in such depth and detail as the competent person considers necessary to enable them to determine whether the equipment being examined is safe to continue in use.

C
07

Appendix B – Case study of lifting operation categorisation

Example activity – Lifting of a generating set and fuel tank with a lorry loader

Situation 1	Straightforward off-load on to level ground beside lorry.		
Environment – 1	Load – 1	Example hazards	Example control measures

Lift categorisation – Basic

Example hazards	Example control measures
Overturning of lorry loader or failure through overloading of the lorry loader attachment or lifting accessory.	▪ Accurately assess the weight of the load. ▪ Accurately assess the maximum radius at which the load can be lifted. ▪ Correctly select the lorry loader and lifting accessories.
Overturning of the lorry loader through ground bearing failure.	Assessment of ground conditions and use of spreader pads.

Lifting team

- Appointed person prepares generic risk assessment and method statement.
- Operator takes the role of crane supervisor, slinger/signaller and operator.

Planning requirements

- Generic risk assessment and method statement.
- On-site review of risk assessment and method statement by crane supervisor.

Situation 2	Lifting a generating set and fuel tank in a pedestrian area with narrow access and restricted view of load.		
Environment – 2	Load – 1	Example hazards	Example control measures

Lift categorisation – Intermediate

Example hazards	Example control measures
Overturning of lorry loader or failure through overloading of the lorry loader attachment or lifting accessory.	▪ Accurately assess the weight of the load. ▪ Accurately assess the maximum radius at which the load can be lifted. ▪ Correctly select the lorry loader and lifting accessories.
Overturning of the lorry loader through ground bearing failure.	Assessment of ground conditions and use of spreader pads.
Operator has restricted view of load.	Use separate slinger/signaller (including use of two-way radio if required).
Ingress of personnel. Lifting near or over persons.	▪ Cordon area off with physical barriers. ▪ Utilise site personnel to monitor the area. ▪ Close area to public access. ▪ Perform lift out of hours.

Lifting team

- Appointed person prepares task and/or site-specific risk assessment and method statement.
- Operator takes the role of crane supervisor and operator.
- Separate slinger/signaller.

Planning requirements

- Task and/or site-specific risk assessment and method statement.
- On-site review of risk assessment and method statement by crane supervisor.
- Cordoning off of lift area by site.
- Agreement between operator and site to fulfil duties of controlling cordoned off area.

Situation 3		Lifting a generating set and fuel tank in an electrical sub-station with overhead cables and unpaved ground.	
Environment – 3	Load – 1	Example hazards	Example control measures
Lift categorisation – Complex 		Overturning of lorry loader or failure through overloading of the lorry loader attachment or lifting accessory.	■ Accurately assess the weight of the load. ■ Accurately assess the maximum radius at which the load can be lifted. ■ Correctly select the lorry loader and lifting accessories.
		Overturning of the lorry loader through ground bearing failure.	Assessment of ground conditions and use of spreader pads.
		Ingress of personnel. Lifting near or over persons.	Cordon area off with physical barriers. Utilise site personnel to monitor the area.
		Electricity cables.	Have power switched off.
		Blind lift.	Dedicated slinger/signaller.
Lifting team ■ Appointed person prepares site-specific risk assessment and method statement. ■ Separate crane supervisor oversees lifting operation. ■ Dedicated slinger/signaller required. ■ Operator takes the role of operator only.		Planning requirements ■ Site-specific risk assessment and method statement. ■ On-site review of risk assessment and method statement by crane supervisor. ■ Cordoning off of lift area by site. ■ Agreement between operator and site to fulfil duties of controlling cordoned off area.	

C
07

Appendix C – Recognised hand signals

Start

Stop

Raise

Lower

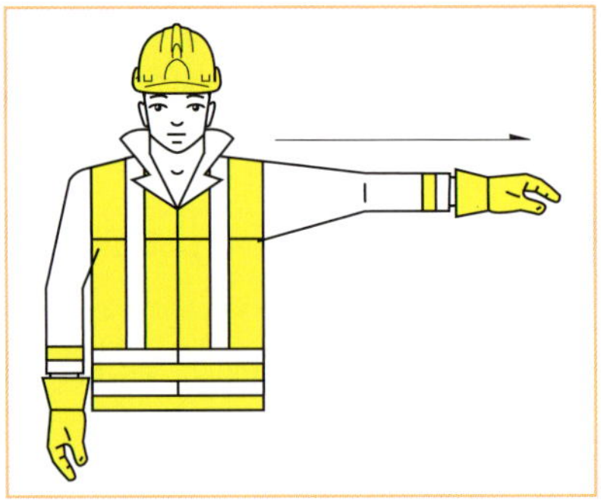

Left

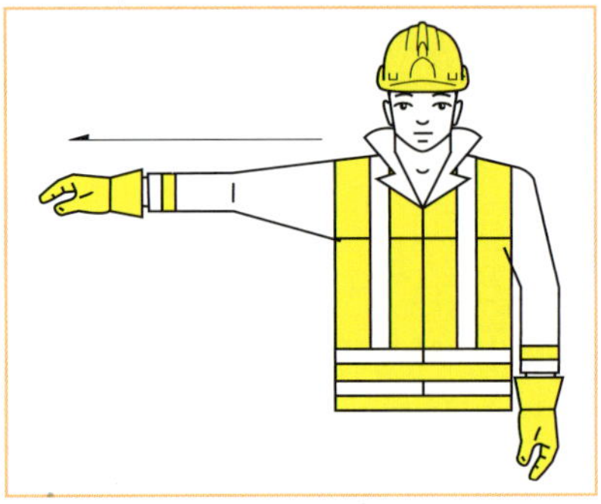

Right

Horizontal distance

Vertical distance

Move backwards

Move forwards

Danger

End

The signaller should stand in a secure position, where they can see the load and can be seen clearly by the lifting equipment operator, and they should face the operator if possible. Each signal should be distinct and clear. These signals have been reproduced from BS 7121-1 *Safe use of cranes – General.*

For further information refer to the HSE publication *Safety signs and signals. The health and safety (Safety signs and signals). Guidance on regulations.*

Appendix D – Information to be contained in a report of thorough examination (Schedule 1 LOLER)

1. The name and address of the employer for whom the thorough examination was made.
2. The address of the premises at which the thorough examination was made.
3. Particulars sufficient to identify the lifting equipment including, where known, its date of manufacture.
4. The date of the last thorough examination.
5. The safe working load of the lifting equipment or (where its safe working load depends on the configuration of the lifting equipment) its safe working load for the last configuration in which it was thoroughly examined.
6. In relation to the first thorough examination of lifting equipment after installation or after assembly at a new site or in a new location:
   - that it is such a thorough examination
   - (if such be the case) that it has been installed correctly and would be safe to operate.
7. For a thorough examination of lifting equipment other than a thorough examination relating to the circumstances in 6 above:
   - whether it is a thorough examination:
     - within an interval of six months under regulation 9(3)(a)(i)
     - within an interval of 12 months under regulation 9(3)(a)(ii)
     - in accordance with an examination scheme under regulation 9(3)(a)(iii)
     - after the occurrence of exceptional circumstances under regulation 9(3)(a)(iv)
   - (if such be the case) that the lifting equipment would be safe to operate.
8. In relation to every thorough examination of lifting equipment:
   - identification of any part found to have a defect, which is or could become a danger to persons, and a description of the defect
   - particulars of any repair, renewal or alteration required to remedy a defect found to be a danger to persons
   - in the case of a defect which is not yet but could become a danger to persons:
     - the time by which it could become such a danger
     - particulars of any repair, renewal or alteration required to remedy it
   - the latest date by which the next thorough examination must be carried out
   - where the thorough examination included testing, particulars of any test
   - the date of the thorough examination.
9. The name, address and qualifications of the person making the report; whether they are self-employed or, if employed, the name and address of their employer.
10. The name and address of a person signing or authenticating the report on behalf of its author.
11. The date of the report.

Appendix E – Wind strengths and effects (Beaufort scale)

Wind force number	Description of wind	Wind effect locally	Speed (mph)	Speed (m/sec)
0	Calm	Calm, smoke rises vertically.	1	0–1
1	Light air	Direction of wind shown by smoke drift, but not by wind or weather vanes.	1–3	1–2
2	Light breeze	Wind felt on face. Leaves rustle. Wind or weather vanes move.	4–7	2–3
3	Gentle breeze	Leaves and small twigs in constant motion. Wind extends light flags.	8–12	3–5
4	Moderate breeze	Wind raises dust and loose paper. Small branches move.	13–18	5–8
5	Fresh breeze	Small trees in leaf begin to sway. Little crested wavelets form on inland waters.	19–24	8–11
6	Strong breeze	Large branches in motion. Umbrellas used with some difficulty.	25–31	11–14
7	Near gale	Whole trees in motion. Becoming difficult to walk against the wind.	32–38	14–17
8	Gale	Twigs break off trees. Progress is generally impeded.	39–46	17–21
9	Strong gale	Chimney pots, slates and tiles may be blown off. Other slight structural damage may be caused.	47–54	21–24

08

Lifting equipment

Contents

Supporting information

G: Checklists and forms

GT 700 Toolbox talks

Overview

Each year there are, on average, six fatalities and a significant number of specified injuries in the construction industry due to lifting operations. The majority of these could have been avoided by effective planning and control of the lifting operations, adequate selection, maintenance, inspection and thorough examination of lifting equipment, and thorough training, assessment and briefing of personnel.

This chapter gives an overview of the requirements for installing, using, checking, maintaining, inspecting and thoroughly examining specific types of lifting equipment and lifting accessories. The general principles of planning and carrying out lifting operations, and undertaking maintenance and thorough examination, are covered in Chapter C07 Lifting operations.

8.1 Introduction

Experience has shown that lifting operations can be a hazardous work activity if not properly planned and carried out. Safe lifting operations will depend upon the following.

- The availability of suitable lifting equipment, which is properly maintained.
- The provision of adequate information, instruction, training or supervision for everyone involved.
- Thorough pre-planning of each lifting operation.
- Compliance with safe systems of work, as detailed in risk assessments and method statements (lifting plan).

Although regulations require that safe systems of work are developed, accidents that have occurred during lifting operations indicate that all too often these are not in place or not complied with if they are in place.

Lifting operations have the potential for death and serious injury to both site workers and members of the public off site. In addition to the terrible cost in human suffering, accidents have a financial cost. There is a very strong business case for improving safety performance.

This chapter is intended to provide advice to non-specialists on the implications that utilising lifting equipment on site will have for them. The content is therefore restricted to information considered relevant for site managers, project managers and others who may become involved in hiring-in lifting equipment or ensuring it is safely used on site. As a consequence, the inclusion of technical information on, for example, the technicalities of lifting equipment construction maintenance, inspection and thorough examination, has been limited.

By way of illustration, whilst it is reasonable to expect a site manager to know when a piece of lifting equipment should be thoroughly examined, detail of the content of such examinations is beyond the scope of this chapter.

C
08

Problems with lifting operations often occur because of poor communications, both during planning and when lifting.

Between 2000 and 2010 there were six major incidents on UK construction sites that involved the collapse of a tower crane.

- **Canary Wharf in 2000.**
- **Worthing in 2005.**
- **Battersea in 2006.**
- **Liverpool in 2007.**
- **Croydon in 2007.**
- **Liverpool in 2009.**

www.

The Health and Safety Executive (HSE) commissioned a report into tower crane incidents worldwide. The RR820 report is available on their website.

For further guidance on lifting equipment refer to the HSE's ACoP and guidance *Safe use of lifting equipment* (L113).

8.2 Important points

- Many accidents occur during lifting operations because they were not properly planned in advance.
- All lifting operations must be carried out by, and under the control of, trained and competent persons who have been properly briefed on the lifting plan.
- The rated capacity of any item of lifting equipment or lifting accessory must never be exceeded.

- All lifting equipment and lifting accessories used for lifting operations must be adequately maintained.
- All lifting equipment and lifting accessories used for lifting operations must be subjected to a schedule of inspections and thorough examinations.
- In addition to the lifting equipment and lifting accessories used, attention must also be paid to site features (such as overhead cables, unstable ground conditions and adjacent properties).
- When using a hired crane, a contract lift will transfer the majority of the legal responsibility for carrying out the lifting operation in a safe manner to the contract lift company.

The collapse, overturning or failure of any load-bearing part of a hoist, crane or other lifting equipment is a notifiable dangerous occurrence, even if nobody is injured.
For further information refer to Chapter A13 Accident reporting and investigation.

8.3 Mobile cranes (wheeled and crawler mounted)

Mobile cranes are lifting equipment that can move under their own power between lifting positions. They are either mounted on wheeled or crawler chassis.

Crawler crane

- Wheeled mobile cranes are generally mounted on either truck crane chassis or all-terrain chassis. Truck cranes are generally restricted to travelling on metalled roads and well-compacted ground on site whilst all-terrain cranes can travel on both public roads and over most site conditions. Some all terrain wheeled cranes may have a limited ability to lift and travel with a load (pick and carry duties). Wheeled mobile cranes range in capacity between 25 tonnes and 1,200 tonnes.
- Crawler mobile cranes require transporting to site in component form on a low loader and other vehicles. Once the crane has been rigged it can travel around the site with ease and lift and travel with a load. Crawler mobile cranes range in capacity from 40 tonnes to 3,000 tonnes.
- Mini or compact cranes are generally mounted on small crawler or wheeled chassis and may be fitted with outriggers to provide stability. Some are fitted with cabs for the operator and have pick and carry duties. Mini crane capacity is generally in the range of one tonne to ten tonnes.

8.3.1 Hired cranes

In construction, mobile cranes are generally hired by the user on site from the crane owner. The two ways of doing this are by hiring a crane (hired crane) or employing a contractor to carry out the lifting operation (contract lift).

The difference between the two options is summarised below.

8.3.1.1 Hired crane (hired and managed)

The employing organisation should complete the following.

- Carry out all work in accordance with BS 7121.
- Supply the competent (appointed) person.
- Plan the lift and operate a safe system of work.
- Ensure that the crane hired is of a suitable type and capacity.
- Check the credentials of the crane company and certification supplied.

The crane owner has a duty to provide a crane that is properly maintained, tested and certified, and a competent operator.

8.3.1.2 Contract lift (fully contracted)

The employing organisation should specify the following.

- That all work is to be undertaken in accordance with BS 7121.
- That the lifting contractor is to supply the competent (appointed) person.
- The dimensions and weight of the load to be lifted.
- The ground bearing capacity.
- What other information and/or services will be provided to the lifting contractor by the employing organisation.

The lifting contractor is responsible for the following.

- Supplying the competent (appointed) person.
- Planning the lift, and operation of a safe system of work.
- Organisation and control of the lifting operation.

If an individual or organisation does not have expertise in lifting operations they should not hire cranes but should opt for a contract lift. Before entering into a contract, users should satisfy themselves that the contractor has the necessary competence to carry out the work.

For further detailed guidance on crane hire and contract lifts refer to the Construction Plant-hire Association's *Crane hire and contract lifting* (Best practice guide).

8.3.2 Planning and use of mobile cranes

The planning and carrying out of lifting operations with mobile cranes should be carried out in accordance with Chapter C07.

For further detailed guidance refer to the *Code of Practice for the safe use of cranes – Part 2-3: Inspection, maintenance and thorough examination – Mobile cranes* (BS 7121-2-3).

8.3.3 Maintenance, checks and inspections of mobile cranes

Mobile cranes should be checked, maintained and inspected in accordance with 7.10 of Chapter C07.

In addition, when planning and carrying out maintenance work on mobile cranes it should not be forgotten that when travelling on the road, the condition of the crane chassis (brakes, suspension, steering, lights, wheels, tyres, and so on) will have a significant effect on the safety of the crane driver and other road users. Although mobile cranes are currently exempt from both the Commercial Vehicle Operators Licensing and Plating and Testing Regulations, the Road Vehicles (Construction and Use) Regulations (Reg. 100) require that they should:

at all times be in such condition ... that no danger is caused or is likely to be caused to any person in or on the vehicle or on a road.

As a mobile crane has the potential to cause as much damage in a road traffic accident as any other large vehicle, it is good practice to follow the recommendations set out in the manufacturer's service manual. These normally set maintenance intervals based on both engine hours run and distance travelled, whereby the first parameter reached determines the need for maintenance.

Failure to maintain the chassis of a mobile crane adequately may put the crane operator and other road users at risk from issues such as those listed below.

- Poor brake performance or failure leading to increased braking distances and an inability to stop in time.
- Insufficient tyre tread grip leading to increased braking distances.
- Hydraulic fluid leaks from the suspension system leading to contamination of the road surface and potential loss of control for other road users.
- Tyre blow-outs leading to loss of control of the crane.
- Steering system failures leading to loss of control of the crane.
- Lighting failures leading to the operator not being able to see clearly and other road users not being able to see the crane.

- Wiper, washer and demister failures preventing the crane operator from seeing clearly.
- Failure of the vehicle suspension system.
- Failure of the crane chassis.
- Security of outrigger plates, covers, guards and other potentially loose items.

It is essential that the chassis of a mobile crane is effectively cleaned before maintenance and inspection is carried out, to ensure that defects can be detected.

For further detailed guidance on the maintenance of mobile cranes refer to the Construction Plant-hire Association's *Maintenance, inspection and thorough examination of mobile cranes* (Best practice guide) and the *Code of Practice for the safe use of cranes – Part 2-3: Inspection, maintenance and thorough examination – Mobile cranes* (BS 7121-2-3).

8.3.4 Thorough examination of mobile cranes

The thorough examination of mobile cranes should be carried out in accordance with 7.11 of Chapter C07.

8.3.5 Four year testing of mobile cranes

In the past, mobile cranes in the UK have frequently been subjected to overload testing at four yearly intervals, in addition to the periodic thorough examinations required by the Lifting Operations and Lifting Equipment Regulations (LOLER). This is a legacy from the requirements of the old Construction (Lifting Operations) Regulations, which were repealed when LOLER was introduced in 1998.

The Approved Code of Practice (ACoP) to LOLER states that any testing is at the discretion of the competent person carrying out a thorough examination and that the competent person will decide on the nature of the test and the method of carrying it out.

Advice from the HSE confirms that four yearly overload testing is no longer a legal requirement and repeated overload testing itself may be dangerous as it may create the conditions for additional faults or even failure during testing.

In the HSE's view the most appropriate method of assessing the condition of a mobile crane is to adopt a defined scope for thorough examination. This is where a specific examination schedule is drawn up for the machine being examined by a competent person, which details the parts of the mobile crane that should be thoroughly examined and the supplementary reports and tests that should be carried out.

For further detailed guidance on the defined scope for the thorough examination of mobile cranes refer to the Construction Plant-hire Association's *Maintenance, inspection and thorough examination of mobile cranes* (Best practice guide) and the *Code of Practice for the safe use of cranes – Part 2-3: Inspection, maintenance and thorough examination – Mobile cranes* (BS 7121-2-3).

8.4 Tower cranes

Tower cranes fall into three main categories.

- **Top slew tower cranes**, which are controlled from a cab at the top of the mast and are erected and dismantled using a large mobile crane, for which provision has to be made in terms of space and stable ground conditions. Top slew tower cranes are further subdivided into saddle jib and luffing jib types.
- **Self-erecting tower cranes**, which are controlled from ground level, often using remote controls, and are self-erecting and folding.
- **Vehicle mounted tower cranes**, which are often controlled remotely from the ground and need to be treated as a mobile crane.

8.4.1 Tower crane installation

When contemplating the erection of a tower crane on site the following points should be taken into account.

- All tower cranes require suitable foundations. For top slew tower cranes particularly, both static and travelling, the foundations will require careful design by a competent engineer.
- Some tower cranes are tied to an adjacent structure for support. The ties and their connections to the crane and the supporting structure will require careful design by a competent engineer.

- On sites where more than one tower crane is erected, there may be overlapping arcs of operation when slewing; anti-clash devices may be fitted or crash radios utilised.
- As a result, the cranes should be erected with their jibs at different heights; crane slewing operations will have to be co-ordinated.
- The required airspace must be confirmed with regard to the proximity of adjacent structures, overhead power lines or other obstructions.
- The requirement for airspace may need to be discussed with any local airport to establish that there will be no intrusion into, or unacceptably near to, aircraft flight paths.
- There may be a requirement for an aircraft warning light or beacon on the highest point of the crane; the colour intensity and whether it is on steady or flashes will depend upon the local rules for any flight path affected.
- Electrically powered tower cranes will require a heavy duty power supply and the crane must be effectively earthed to protect against electrical faults and lightning strikes, including earthing of the appropriate rails. The requirements of the Electricity at Work Act apply to all electrically powered tower cranes and their power supply.
- In many cases they have the capacity to over-sail adjacent properties and areas to which the public have access; arrangements will have to be made with the appropriate authorities.
- Where the right to over-sail adjacent property is not given, it may be necessary to:
  - rearrange siting of the tower crane(s)
  - review the type of crane required (for example, a luffing jib crane might be the only solution).

For detailed guidance on the design and installation of tower crane bases and ties refer to the Construction Industry Research and Information Association's *Tower crane stability* (C654).

For further detailed guidance on the erection, climbing and dismantling of tower cranes refer to the British Standard *Safe use of cranes – Tower cranes* (BS 7121-5) and the Construction Plant-hire Association's *Climbing of tower cranes* (Best practice guide).

C
08

8.4.2 Planning and use of tower cranes

The planning and carrying out of lifting operations with tower cranes should be in accordance with the principles set out in Chapter C07. In addition, the following points should be taken into account.

- High winds can temporarily stop tower crane operations; each crane should be fitted with an anemometer (wind-speed indicator).
- In high winds, tower cranes must be left in free slew with their hooks raised.
- A plan for rescue from height must be in place in the event of an accident or incident (for example, the operator becoming ill). The emergency services have no obligation to carry out such rescues and are often not able to assist because of the height of the rescue and because of restricted access for large vehicles (such as fire service turntable ladders).

For further detailed guidance on rescue from height on tower cranes refer to the Construction Plant-hire Association's Technical information note 013.

Tower cranes must be secured against unauthorised access, including climbing the tower and unauthorised use.

A lifting plan, approved by the competent (appointed) person, must be in place.

For further detailed guidance on the safe use of tower cranes refer to:

- ***Safe use of cranes – Tower cranes* (BS 7121-5)**
- **Construction Plant-hire Association's (Best practice guide):**
  - ***Safe use of top slew tower cranes***
  - ***Safe use of self-erecting tower cranes***
  - ***Tower crane working conditions***
  - ***Tower crane operations – Minimum competency requirements.***

8.4.3 Maintenance, checks and inspections of tower cranes

Tower cranes should be checked, maintained and inspected in accordance with 7.10 of Chapter C07.

8.4.4 Thorough examination of tower cranes

The thorough examination of tower cranes should be carried out in accordance with 7.11 of Chapter C07.

For further detailed guidance on the maintenance, inspection and thorough examination of tower cranes refer to the Construction Plant-hire Association's *Maintenance, inspection and thorough examination of tower cranes* (Best practice guide) and the *Code of Practice for the safe use of cranes – Part 2-5: Inspection, maintenance and thorough examination – Tower cranes* (BS 7121-2-5).

8.4.5 Tower crane register

The Notification of Conventional Tower Crane Regulations, which required conventional tower cranes used on construction sites to be notified to the HSE, were revoked on 6 April 2013. Instead, the HSE is now encouraging contractors to participate in the *Safe crane campaign* and display the campaign poster outside their sites.

Further information on the *Safe crane campaign* can be found on the Construction Plant-hire Association website.

8.5 Lorry loaders

Lorry loaders were originally designed to load and unload goods onto and off the body of the vehicle on which they were mounted so that deliveries and collections did not have to rely on other loading and unloading facilities.

In recent years lorry loaders have developed significantly and are now able to carry out many of the tasks traditionally undertaken by mobile and tower cranes. When used safely they make a valuable contribution to lifting operations. However, it should not be forgotten that all lifting operations must be planned and executed to the same standard, irrespective of the type of lifting equipment being used.

Unfortunately over the past few years there have been a significant number of accidents involving lorry loaders, which have included fatalities. These could have been prevented by correct planning, supervision, use and maintenance. In addition to the cost in human suffering, accidents have a financial cost. There is a strong business case for improving safety performance.

For further information refer to the Construction Plant-hire Association's *Work at height whilst loading and unloading transport* (Best practice guide).

8.5.1 Types of lorry loader

A lorry loader is a commercial vehicle or trailer fitted with a loader crane. Loader cranes have a column that slews about its base and a boom system that is attached to the top of the column.

Typical lorry loader

Lorry loaders are rated in terms of load movement and are available in sizes from 0.5 tonne metre to 84 tonne metre.

When in use, the lorry loader is generally stabilised by two stabilisers mounted on the loader crane base. In the past loader crane controls were mounted at the base of the column, but today they are normally portable wireless units that give the operator greater flexibility of movement and help to keep the load in view.

8.5.2 Planning and use of lorry loaders

The planning and carrying out of lifting operations with lorry loaders should be in accordance with the principles set out in Chapter C07.

8.5.3 Maintenance, checks and inspections of lorry loaders

Lorry loaders should be checked, maintained and inspected in accordance with 7.10 of Chapter C07.

8.5.4 Thorough examination of lorry loaders

The thorough examination of lorry loaders should be carried out in accordance with 7.11 of Chapter C07.

For detailed guidance on the safe use of lorry loaders refer to the Construction Plant-hire Association's *Safe use of lorry loaders* (Best practice guide).

8.6 Mobile elevating work platforms

MEWPs are designed to provide temporary working platforms which, when people are in the work platform, can be easily adjusted for height and outreach. They can also be easily moved from one location to another and are particularly suitable for tasks where the use of a ladder would be unsafe and the erection of a scaffolding platform too time-consuming or impracticable in relation to the job to be done.

Sizes and capabilities of MEWPs vary considerably. Small, one-person machines are available, with a maximum safe working load of 120 kg, and working heights of a few metres, whilst at the other end of the scale, work platforms may be 4 m x 2 m or more and have safe working loads in excess of 1,000 kg. Extending boom heights can exceed 100 metres and the outreach of some units can approach 40 metres.

8.6.1 Types of mobile elevating work platform

The basic types of MEWP elevating structure (the part that lifts the work platform) are listed below.

- Scissor lifts.
- Vertical lifts.
- Telescopic booms.
- Articulating and telescopic booms or multi-boom articulated.

These elevating structures may be mounted on chassis that are towable units, vehicles, self-propelled (wheeled or crawler) or pedestrian controlled.

C
08

8.6.1.1 Scissor lift

This type of MEWP gives a substantially vertical lift. The work platform may be fitted with a sliding extension that will give a small amount of outreach.

8.6.1.2 Vertical lift

This type of MEWP gives vertical lift only and is generally used for small, lightweight machines for indoor use only.

8.6.1.3 Telescopic boom

This type gives both vertical height and outreach, and the telescoping function gives smooth and fine control near structures. The work platform may also be able to swivel in the horizontal plane and is mounted on a fly jib for additional manoeuvrability. Boom-type MEWPs are sometimes known as cherry pickers.

8.6.1.4 Articulating and telescopic or multi-boom articulated

These types of MEWP may be mounted on a road-going vehicle chassis or a self-propelled wheeled or crawler chassis. They give a wide range of reach and height. Vehicle-mounted MEWPs are nearly always equipped with outriggers and specialised types are available (for example, machines that enable access to the underside of bridge arches from the roadway above).

Units mounted on a self-propelled chassis have a 'travel while elevated' ability and may have four-wheel drive. Rough-terrain MEWPs have been specially developed for construction site work.

8.6.2 Planning and use of MEWPs

The planning and carrying out of lifting operations with MEWPs should be in accordance with the principles set out in Chapter C07. In addition the points below should be taken into account.

8.6.2.1 Entrapment of people on the platform

In certain circumstances (such as working at height amongst steelwork) there is an increased risk to people in the work platform of a MEWP of becoming trapped, and in some cases crushed, between the platform and a fixed obstruction. There have been a number of such incidents in the UK over the past few years, several of which have resulted in fatalities. Job planning should consider this hazard and, where required, additional measures should be taken.

- Consideration of additional safety devices on the MEWP.
- Devising and implementing a rescue plan for people trapped at height.
- Briefing of operators and other people in the work platform.

This issue has been highlighted by the HSE as a result of several accidents in which MEWP operators had become injured and immobilised but were unable to release themselves, having become trapped between the machine (such as the top guard-rail or controls) and a fixed structure (often structural steelwork).

For comprehensive guidance on avoiding entrapment refer to the Strategic Forum for Construction Plant Safety Group's *MEWPs – Avoiding trapping/crushing injuries to people in the platform* (Best practice guide).

8.6.2.2 Emergency controls

Both ground and work platform controls should be checked as part of the pre-use inspection to ensure they are working correctly. This check should also include the emergency lowering controls, which are provided to enable the work platform to be safely recovered to ground level and all emergency stop controls.

The operator, or their supervisor, should ensure that a responsible person, who is familiar with the emergency lowering system, is always in close proximity to the MEWP, to lower the work platform in the event that rescue is required.

Emergency descent decal

This image can be used on MEWPs, in conjunction with existing manufacturer's symbols, to aid location of the emergency controls.

Even experienced operators sometimes have difficulty locating the emergency descent controls that every MEWP is fitted with.

This decal is a practical visual aid and a prime example of an industry initiative to make access equipment even safer.

Emergency descent systems can be found on all types of MEWPs. They differ in terms of where they are located on specific machines and how they operate.

The decal should be positioned to clearly indicate the location of the emergency descent controls. Operators should ensure that somebody at ground level is properly trained on how to use the controls and can gain access to the decal in an emergency.

Personnel must never attempt to climb out of an elevated MEWP if the emergency back-up system fails to work, but should stay in the work platform until rescued by other means.

This decal is available to download free from the IPAF website.

8.6.3 Overturning

- Check for soft ground, drains and other unsuitable ground conditions before deploying the outriggers or stabilisers; check for the hazard before siting the machine.
- Beware of overloading, especially if the work platform is being used at maximum outreach to remove fans, motors or other heavy loads. Always observe the safe working load.
- Be careful when operating on a slope, even if the machine is properly levelled with the stabilisers or outriggers.
- Always check that the machine is stable before operating.
- Be careful when travelling with the work platform raised, especially on poor ground conditions.

- ☑ Never attempt to travel while the outriggers or stabilisers are deployed, unless the machine is designed for this purpose.
- ☑ Be careful not to collide with any obstruction or other vehicle.
- ☑ Some modern machines are fitted with a tilt sensor, which, if activated, only enables the work platform to be lowered.

8.6.4 Fall protection

The following refers predominantly to the use of boom-type MEWPs although, in some circumstances, parts could also be relevant to the use of scissor or other vertical lifts. Personal fall protection systems fall into two categories: work-restraint systems and fall-arrest systems.

8.6.4.1 Work-restraint system

Whereas fall-arrest equipment allows a person to fall but arrests the fall before the person hits the surface below, work-restraint equipment prevents the fall from happening.

The main feature of work-restraint equipment is that a shorter lanyard is used, which restricts the operator's limit of travel to the confines of the work platform.

Lanyards should be carefully selected, taking into account the features of the machine on which they are to be used, to ensure that the user cannot get into a situation where a fall could occur. The lanyard must always be attached to a designated anchor point in the work platform.

A fall-arrest lanyard **can** be used for restraint but a restraint lanyard may **not** be used for fall arrest.

8.6.4.2 Fall-arrest system

Where a decision has been taken to rely on fall-arrest equipment as a means of preventing injury, it will be necessary for the operator to wear a full body harness and a lanyard equipped with an energy absorber. Vital considerations are shown below.

- ☑ The height at which work is being carried out must be such that it allows the lanyard to arrest the fall and the energy absorber to deploy before the wearer hits the surface below. A minimum working height of 6.75 m is recommended if fall-arrest is to operate successfully.
- ☑ The anchor point on the machine must have been designed to withstand the shock-loading of arresting a fall. Many anchor points fitted to MEWPs are only rated for work restraint. If the anchor point is not marked with its rating, contact the manufacturer to find it out.
- ☑ Users of harness and lanyard must have been trained in their use, inspection and care.
- ☑ In arresting a fall, a boom-type MEWP will flex, which could eject other occupants and materials out of the basket. This could also overturn the machine if it is operating at maximum outreach.
- ☑ A check must be made that the structure has no projecting features that the falling person would strike during the fall.
- ☑ How the person who has fallen will be rescued after the fall has been arrested. This may be as simple as another operator gently lowering the boom of a MEWP using the ground level controls until the fallen person is at ground level.

An exception to wearing a harness whilst operating a MEWP is when the machine is working over, or near to, water.

A safety harness must never be attached to anything outside the work platform; operation of the controls in this situation could leave the user suspended in mid-air *(see illustration above)*.

For further information on the use of personal fall protection equipment in MEWPs refer to the HSE's *Preventing falls from boom-type mobile elevating work platforms* (MISC 614).

For advice on the inspection of harnesses and lanyards refer to the HSE information sheet *Inspecting fall-arrest equipment made from webbing or rope* (INDG367).

C 08

8.6.5 Working over, or near to, water

There could be a danger of drowning where a MEWP, particularly an articulating boom-type machine (cherry picker), is being used over, or near to, water. It is possible that the work platform of such a machine could come to rest underwater if it were to topple over. It is essential, therefore, that the occupant(s) of the work platform do **not** clip on to the anchorage point, as would happen normally (or elsewhere around the working platform) and do wear lifejackets.

In such circumstances:

- even though the machine toppling would have a traumatic effect on the user(s), they still might have a chance of being able to swim to, or scramble back onto, dry land
- a risk assessment must be carried out to determine and implement effective fall prevention measures that would normally be covered by wearing a harness and lanyard.

8.6.6 Restricted or enclosed spaces

- Extra care is needed when working in, or manoeuvring into, restricted or confined spaces to avoid collisions and/or entrapment. A full and precise understanding of all controls is essential.
- If the MEWP has an internal combustion engine, remember that the exhaust fumes will cause a hazard in any confined or enclosed space.
- Batteries for units should not be charged in enclosed spaces. There is a hazard of explosive hydrogen gases being given off.
- Liquefied petroleum gas (LPG) powered vehicles should not be refuelled in a confined space. Any spillage of fuel will quickly and dramatically expand into a large gas cloud. The gas will then accumulate at the lowest point and create an explosive hazard.

8.6.7 Interference with MEWPs in public places

- Whenever MEWPs are used in public places, additional precautions should be taken to ensure segregation between members of the public and the machine. This may be by the use of barriers or posting marshals around the machine.
- Additional interlocks or guards may be necessary to prevent the operation of, or tampering with, ground level controls by unauthorised persons or children.
- Care should be taken against the risk of entrapment as a result of inquisitive people, and especially children, getting too close or underneath. Scissor lifts are particularly hazardous.

C 08

For further detailed guidance on the planning and safe use of MEWPs refer to:

- ***Code of Practice for the safe use of MEWPs*** **(BS 8460)**
- **HSE Construction information sheet *Selection and management of mobile elevating work platforms* (CIS 58).**

8.6.8 Maintenance, checks and inspections of MEWPs

MEWPs should be checked, maintained and inspected in accordance with 7.10 of Chapter C07.

8.6.9 Thorough examination of MEWPs

The thorough examination of MEWPs should be carried out in accordance with 7.11 of Chapter C07.

8.7 Construction hoists

Hoists of various types are widely used on construction sites. These range from high capacity passenger/goods hoists, goods only hoists, transport platforms, inclined hoists, scaffold hoists and trestle/beam hoists, to the humble gin wheel.

Passenger/goods hoists, goods only hoists, transport platforms and inclined hoists, where the load is guided, are often referred to as construction hoists, to distinguish them from scaffold hoists, trestle/beam hoists and gin wheels, where the load is not guided.

As pressure increases to become more efficient and reduce manual handling, hoists are an increasingly vital part of many construction operations. The smooth and rapid movement of persons and materials assists in efficient management of projects. Even where other methods of moving materials around site are to be used (for example, by a tower crane) it is not unusual to find a hoist used solely to assist the scaffold erection process.

The number and type of scaffold hoists and trestle/beam hoists available for hire has increased significantly and their use will require a lifting plan (*refer to Chapter C07*) to be drawn up by a competent person. This plan must consider possible exclusion zones under the hoist in the event of the load dropping, safe slinging methods, the appropriate lifting accessories, and so on. These are a different set of risks compared with, for example, loads being carried in the enclosed platform of a goods hoist.

Risks can arise from a late decision to use a hoist to solve a previously unforeseen problem during the construction phase. For example, if planning to use a hoist tied to a scaffolding system that is already in place but which was not originally designed to take the additional loadings, there is a need for careful planning and discussions with the scaffold designer before simply allowing a hoist to be hired and fixed to the scaffold.

Except for manually operated hoists and any that have an independent power supply, the requirement for a dedicated power supply to the hoist must also be considered. Most hoists are electrically powered, so the Electricity at Work Regulations will apply to the installation. The electrical power requirements may result in the need for generators, which must be of adequate capacity. This introduces potential noise, fuel storage and spillage issues.

8.7.1 Types of hoist

A wide range of hoists are used on construction sites. The main types are described below.

8.7.1.1 Passenger/goods hoists

- Have a rack and pinion drive mechanism.
- Are tied to an adjacent structure.
- Can be erected to lifting heights of up to 250 m.
- Can travel at up to 100 m per minute.
- Are operated from inside the cage.
- Are available in a wide range of cage sizes, up to 1.5 m wide x 4.6 m long.
- Are available with payloads of up to 3,200 kg.

8.7.1.2 Goods only hoists

- Generally have a rack and pinion drive mechanism.
- Are tied to an adjacent structure.
- Can be erected to lifting heights of up to 100 m.
- Can travel at up to 40 m per minute.
- Are operated from outside the cage.
- Are available in a wide range of cage sizes, from 1.4 m wide x 0.8 m long, to 1.5 m wide x 6.0 m long.
- Are available with payloads from 200 kg up to 2,500 kg.

C
08

8.7.1.3 Transport platforms

Transport platforms are dual-purpose machines that either carry goods only, in which case they are operated from outside the platform, or carry passengers, in which case they are operated from inside the platform and are restricted to a speed of 12 metres per minute.

For detailed guidance on transport platforms refer to the Construction Plant-hire Association's *Transport platforms – Installation, use, maintenance, inspection, examination and testing* (Best practice guide).

8.7.1.4 Inclined hoists

- Generally have a wire rope drive mechanism.
- Are supported by an adjacent structure.
- Can be erected to lifting heights of up to 40 m.
- Can travel at up to 25 m per minute.
- Are operated from outside the platform.
- Have platforms of about 0.7 m x 0.8 m.
- Are available with payloads up to 250 kg.

8.7.1.5 Scaffold hoists

Scaffold hoists are not hoists in the true sense, in that the load is not guided, as is the case with a goods or passenger/goods hoist. They are in fact small cranes that are generally attached to scaffolding, having a small swinging jib on which is mounted a wire rope winch.

- Have a lifting capacity of up to 250 kg.
- Have a standard lifting height of up to 50 m.
- Can lift at up to 25 m per minute.

8.7.1.6 Trestle/beam hoists

Trestle/beam or gantry hoists consist of a runway beam mounted in a trestle structure, with a wire rope winch mounted on the beam. The beam is cantilevered over the edge of a building roof or floor, enabling materials to be lifted from ground level.

- Have a lifting capacity of up to 1,000 kg.
- Have a standard lifting height of up to 25 m.
- Can lift at up to 20 m per minute.

8.7.2 Planning and installation of hoists

The installation of hoists requires good planning and co-ordination and must be undertaken by competent individuals. All hoists must be supplied and, where appropriate, erected, altered and dismantled by companies or people who are fully aware of the legal requirements and the relevant British and European Standards. Special attention must be given to ground conditions to ensure adequate support for the hoist. The forces imposed on the structure by the hoist, its loads and inclement weather, particularly high winds, must also be taken into account. Hoist operators must be adequately trained, competent and authorised and should be specifically responsible for ensuring that the hoist is not overloaded or otherwise misused.

8.7.2.1 Pre-planning (construction hoists)

When it has been decided (ideally at the tender stage) that a construction hoist will be required on site, requirements must be quantified as follows.

- Consideration of the locations for siting the hoist.
- The loads to be carried in terms of size and weight and whether goods only or both goods and passengers are to be carried.
- The likely loading on the structure and whether any enabling work or structural changes are required.
- Any constraints in the position where the hoist can be erected and whether other features (such as scaffolds) must be modified to accommodate the hoist.
- The loading on the hoist's foundations.

At an appropriate point both the user of the hoist (for example, the principal contractor) and the supplier of the hoist should each assign a competent (appointed) person who must liaise with each other to ensure that all aspects of the hoist selection, delivery, erection and use are carried out safely. The user's competent (appointed) person may need to rely upon the experience and competence of the supplier's competent (appointed) person in order to fulfil their responsibilities.

The detailed requirements of these roles, both of which require specific training and previous relevant experience, are considered to be outside the scope of this chapter.

For further information refer to the *Code of Practice for the safe use of construction hoists* (BS 7212).

A full and detailed risk assessment should be carried out before a hoist is positioned. A method statement can then be developed, which must then be agreed with the user.

8.7.2.2 Site survey

Prior to delivery of the hoist it will be necessary for both competent (appointed) persons to visit the site to establish the practicalities of installing it. During the site survey the supplier's appointed person will determine the appropriate type of hoist required, based upon the criteria and information on intended usage of the hoist provided by the user's appointed person.

The findings of the survey will determine the optimum position for the hoist, based upon factors such as those listed below.

- Co-location with materials storage areas.
- Avoidance of hazardous features (such as overhead cables).
- The need for safe access at all levels.
- The need for safe access to the cage or platform at ground level.
- The need for foundations and drainage.
- Suitable locations on the building structure for the attachment of ties.

In selecting the most appropriate hoist, the supplier's appointed person will have to take into account factors such as those listed below.

- The space constraints of the area.
- Access implications relating to the size and weight of the hoist components.
- Ground conditions and suitable locations on the building structure for the attachment of ties.
- The proximity of site features (such as overhead power lines, railway tracks and adjacent public thoroughfares).
- Other work that will take place whilst the hoist is in place and how the site might change during this period.
- Foreseeable extremes in weather conditions.

8.7.2.3 Erecting, altering and dismantling hoists

Hoists that rest on the ground must only be erected on a firm base, adequately supported and secured. All materials supporting the hoist must be strong enough to support the weight of the completed hoist structure and its maximum load, and be free from defects.

The erection of the hoist must be carried out in accordance with the manufacturer's instructions and a method statement that has been discussed with and approved by the user, as the proposed method and timing may impact upon other site work.

Potential problems caused by the loadings that hoists can put on the adjacent structure have already been outlined under the heading of the Construction (Design and Management) Regulations (CDM).

Refer to Chapter C07 Lifting operations.

In many ways, erection, alteration and dismantling are potentially the most hazardous work associated with hoists on site. Anyone not directly involved in erecting the hoist should keep clear of the area.

Planning how the hoist will be erected and deciding who is responsible for what is vital when implementing a safe system of work. This is particularly important where the hoist will be built in conjunction with the erection of a scaffold. It is essential that the erection, and later modification and dismantling, of hoists are properly planned, adequately supervised and carried out in a safe manner by competent persons.

Where the hoist is attached to and supported by a scaffold, the scaffold must be designed to take account of the imposed loadings. This becomes more important where the use of a larger capacity hoist is being considered.

Hoists should be erected by competent personnel holding a Construction Skills Certificate Scheme (CSCS) card and an NVQ in Hoist installation, Level 2 or 3.

8.7.2.4 Use of part-erected hoists

It is common practice for scaffolders to build three or four lifts of scaffold, raising the components by hand, followed by the hoist company erecting the hoist to the height of the scaffold. Further erection of the part-completed hoist is co-ordinated with the scaffold contractors so that it can be used for hoisting scaffold components, as it follows the scaffold up. In such circumstances, normal safe working practices may not be practical.

The rules regarding the interlocking of landing gates cannot be applied when some of the gates have not been installed. Detailed guidance is available and it is strongly recommended that anyone faced with this situation on their site obtains and reads it.

The guidance is published jointly by the National Access and Scaffolding Federation and the Construction Plant-hire Association and is available from both organisations.

For further detailed guidance refer to the Construction Plant-hire Association's *Transporting scaffolding in construction hoists* (Best practice guide).

8.7.2.5 Work at height

Some work at height is unavoidable when carrying out the erection, maintenance, alteration or dismantling of hoists. Work at height must always be planned in accordance with the hierarchy set out in the Work at Height Regulations.

For further detailed guidance refer to the Construction Plant-hire Association's *Work at height on construction hoists* (CHIG 0901).

8.7.2.6 Alteration

Alteration of hoists (such as increasing or decreasing the height) should be planned and carried out in the same way as erection.

8.7.2.7 Dismantling

Dismantling operations should be planned and carried out in the same way as erection. Care should be taken to ensure that adequate time is allowed in the construction programme to ensure that dismantling can be carried out without time pressures on the dismantling team. Before dismantling starts it is essential to ensure that the hoist is in a satisfactory condition for safe dismantling.

8.7.3 Safety of hoistways, platforms and cages

Where necessary to prevent injury, hoistways and/or the hoisting machinery must be segregated by a substantial enclosure at ground level. Suitable barriers must be installed at all other access points, over the full height of travel, and wherever persons could be struck by any moving part, to prevent injury and/or falls.

Consideration must be given to the area around the base of the hoist with regard to loading and unloading materials, and whether a ramp or pit is required to facilitate access to the cage or platform.

The area between the cage or platform and the host structure (the threshold) must be suitably protected to prevent any person or material falling through the gap at each landing.

8.7.3.1 Landings and gates

Where access to a construction hoist is required at several levels, consideration must be given to the space requirements at each landing with regard to loading and unloading the hoist. It is essential that each landing and threshold (the area between the platform and landing) can withstand the loads that will be imposed, with particular emphasis on items, such as pallet trucks, which can impose significant point loading.

The mechanical or electrical features of the hoist should ensure that the gates at any landing point cannot be opened unless the cage or platform is at that landing point, and the cage or platform cannot be set in motion unless all of the landing gates are closed and locked.

For further detailed guidance on landing and gating requirements for goods hoists refer to the Construction Plant-hire Association's *Safeguarding requirements for landing gates of goods-only hoists* (Best practice guide) (CHIG 0401).

8.7.3.2 Handover

Once erected, the hoist will be subjected to a thorough examination, after which the supplier's appointed person should arrange to formally hand over the hoist to the user's appointed person.

The user's appointed person should arrange for all trained operators to be present at the handover of the hoist to receive:

- familiarisation training on the use of the hoist in normal operations
- instruction on what to do in emergency situations
- instruction on how to carry out the daily, pre-use inspections and weekly inspections.

A handover report, containing details of the instruction given, should be passed to the user's appointed person.

For detailed guidance on the planning and installation of construction hoists refer to the *Code of Practice for the safe use of construction hoists* (BS 7212-2).

8.7.4 Planning and use of construction hoists

The planning and carrying out of lifting operations with construction hoists should be in accordance with the principles set out in Chapter C07. In addition, the points below should be taken into account.

8.7.4.1 Operation of hoists

It is essential that only operators who have been trained in the use of the hoist are allowed to operate it. The operator should:

- know the rated load of the hoist
- be able to accurately assess the weight and distribution of any load brought on to the hoist, and therefore identify if it is overloaded
- have access to accurate wind-speed figures and be aware of any limitations placed on the hoist
- be able to lower the hoist to the next landing in the event of a power failure (passenger carrying hoists only)
- carry out daily, pre-use checks and weekly inspections, and take the appropriate follow-up action as necessary. On some complex hoists, it may be necessary for the weekly inspection to be carried out by an employee of the hoist company.

Each hoist should only be capable of being operated from one position at any one time. Where, as in the case of a goods only hoist, the operator is not carried on the platform, they must have a clear view at all levels from the operating position or, if they have not, arrangements must be made for signals to be given to them at each level.

Whatever the system of signalling used, it must be distinct and clear to the person being signalled.

It is reasonable to expect that the hoist operator and the person(s) giving signals are at least 18 years of age. It is not illegal for younger people to do this work, but under regulations a specific risk assessment would need to be carried out to ensure that immaturity had been considered. Irrespective of their age, hoist operators must be trained and competent, unless under constant supervision by a competent person for the purpose of training.

8.7.4.2 Safety notices

The platform of a goods hoist must carry a notice stating:

- ☑ the safe working load
- ☑ that passengers must not ride on the hoist
- ☑ any restrictions regarding load position and concentration.

Cages for passenger hoists must carry a notice stating:

- ☑ the safe working load
- ☑ the maximum number of passengers that can be carried
- ☑ any restrictions regarding load position and concentration.

Landing gates for goods only hoists must carry a notice stating:

- ☑ goods only hoist
- ☑ no passengers
- ☑ keep gates closed
- ☑ rated load in kg.

Landing gates for passenger/goods hoists must carry a notice stating:

- ☑ keep gates closed
- ☑ rated load in kg.

8.7.5 Carriage of persons in hoists

No person should be carried by a hoist, unless it is a designated passenger/goods hoist or transport platform and it is provided with the following.

- ☑ Gates that shut to prevent persons falling out or being trapped between the cage and any other part.
- ☑ An efficient interlocking device, which ensures that gates can only be operated when the cage is at the landing place, and that the cage cannot be moved until the gate is closed.
- ☑ An efficient automatic overrun device to ensure the cage will come to rest at its lowest and highest points of travel.

The construction of the cage or platform must be such as to protect passengers from falling objects. No person should be allowed to travel in a hoist that is designated a goods only hoist.

8.7.6 Security of loads

All loads must be secured to prevent any part from slipping and falling.

Loose materials (for example, bricks and slates) must be lifted in a properly designed box, cage or other container. The platform of a goods only hoist should have sides with a minimum height of 0.6 m or 1.1 m high, if persons can access the platform during loading or unloading.

For detailed guidance on the planning and use of construction hoists refer to the *Code of Practice for safe use of construction hoists* (BS 7212).

8.7.7 Maintenance, checks and inspections of construction hoists

Construction hoists should be checked, maintained and inspected in accordance with 7.10 of Chapter C07.

8.7.8 Thorough examination of construction hoists

The thorough examination of construction hoists should be carried out in accordance with 7.11 of Chapter C07.

For further detailed guidance on the maintenance, inspection and thorough examination of construction hoists refer to the Construction Plant-hire Association's *Maintenance, inspection and thorough examination of construction hoists* (Best practice guide).

8.7.9 Specific requirements for scaffold hoists, trestle/beam hoists, inclined hoists and gin wheels

Scaffold hoists, trestle/beam hoists and inclined hoists are now commonly used throughout the construction industry. These can be easily transported to the site, are quickly erected and require little operating space. They may be fitted with buckets, skips, platforms or cages.

Different models allow for basic height variations of between 8 m and 30 m, although much greater heights can be reached with extensions. Load capacity varies with the model but lifting capacity of 500 kg is not uncommon.

This equipment all comes within the scope of LOLER and, although free standing, are subject to the same provisions as construction hoists that are tied to a structure.

8.7.9.1 Scaffold cranes or barrow hoists

These are lifting equipment within the meaning of the regulations and, as with all lifting equipment, must not be overloaded.

The attachment of scaffold hoists to scaffolds is critical and must be carried out in accordance with the manufacturer's instructions. Scaffold hoists should not be attached to scaffolds unless the scaffolding has been designed to take the loads imposed by the scaffold hoist.

Maintenance, inspection and thorough examination should follow the requirements for cranes in 7.10 and 7.11 of Chapter C07.

8.7.9.2 Trestle/beam hoists

These are lifting equipment as defined by LOLER.

They rely for their stability on counterweighting at the rear of the trestle frame and it is essential that adequate counterweights are supplied. Counterweight is often provided by filling bins attached to the frame with sand or gravel.

Before using the hoist, checks should be made to ensure that sufficient material has been added to the bins and that they are in good condition so that the ballast cannot leak out.

Maintenance, inspection and thorough examination should follow the requirements for cranes in 7.10 and 7.11 of Chapter C07.

8.7.9.3 Inclined hoists

These are lifting equipment within the meaning of the regulations. They are particularly useful for trades such as bricklaying and traditional roofing and indeed, on a larger project, they have the potential to eliminate a significant amount of manual handling.

Inclined hoists are also known as roof tile or brick carriers. New developments include telescopic and slewing functions. Load capacities go up to 200 kg and lateral extensions may be up to 35 m.

Inclined hoists are specifically designed for use at angles between 10° and 85°, and they may also incorporate a hinged section to allow the hoist to follow the pitch of a roof.

They also provide flexible solutions to the problems of removing demolition waste in refurbishment situations. As they are in effect a conveyor-belt system, care needs to be taken to ensure that the guards to the rollers are in place to ensure that fingers and/or clothing cannot be dragged in. These are so called 'in-running nips' and particularly where the motor driving the hoist is powerful the potential for serious injury is significant.

Maintenance, inspection and thorough examination should follow the requirements for construction hoists.

8.7.9.4 Gin wheels

In many cases provision has to be made to raise tools and light materials manually with a rope and gin wheel or single block. Whilst these are still in common use, modern variants are available and incorporate an automatic locking mechanism to prevent the load from going into free-fall if the hoisting rope is accidentally released.

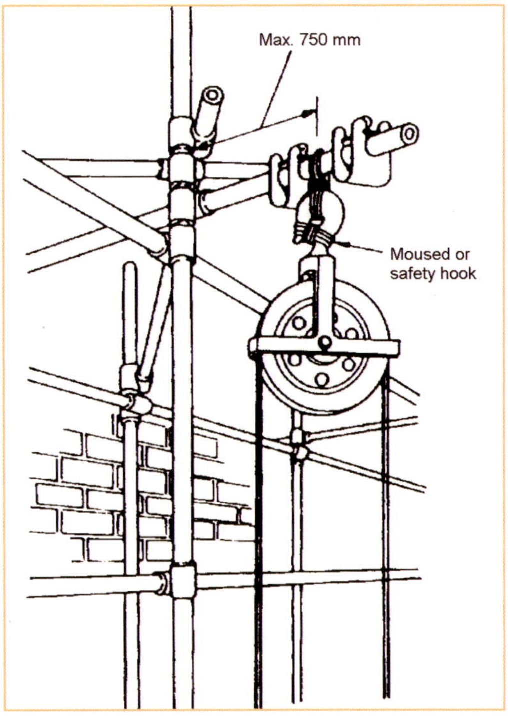

Gin wheel

The following provisions and requirements apply to gin wheels connected to a scaffold.

- ☑ Any scaffold tubes and hooks should be strong enough to take the load that is to be lifted and be properly secured to prevent movement.
- ☑ All ropes should comply with the relevant BS EN standards and fit the wheel correctly. They should be marked with a tag confirming their safe working load.
- ☑ Preferably, the gin wheel should be suspended from a ring-type fitting passed over the end of the supporting tube and secured against lateral movement by scaffold fittings. If using a hook type, it should be properly lashed and moused *(see diagram on left)*.
- ☑ Any joints in standards should be made with sleeve couplers.
- ☑ Gin wheels should be suspended not more than 750 mm from the outer scaffold standard.
- ☑ Hooks used for supporting materials should be safety hooks and spliced into the rope.
- ☑ The maximum load should be no more than 50 kg at 750 mm from the outer scaffold standard.

Whilst of simple construction, gin wheels are categorised as lifting equipment so must be thoroughly examined before use and then at least every 12 months, with a test certificate issued.

Similarly, the lifting accessories used (such as the rope, hook and shackles) must be thoroughly examined before use and then at least every six months.

Given the scope for the harsh treatment of this type of equipment, all parts of a gin wheel assembly should be thoroughly examined at least every six months.

The extent of any thorough examination should reflect the risks that would arise from its failure.

8.8 Mast climbing work platforms

A mast climbing work platform (MCWP) is a form of temporary working platform giving variable height access to structures. They can be automated or mechanised.

They allow efficient work on the façade of buildings and may therefore be the best and safest way, as well as perhaps the most economical, to undertake the work, as opposed to working off a ladder or from a suspended cradle. MCWPs are commonly used during work such as window replacement, lift shaft installation, curtain walling, bricklaying, cleaning and refurbishment.

8.8.1 Training

In order to use a MCWP safely on site training is available for mobile operators, demonstrators, installers and advanced installers.

Demonstrators are responsible for inducting users and ensuring that the equipment is used safely. They need to understand model-specific servicing and engineering details.

Installers, who install the platforms, must have detailed understanding and experience in erection and dismantling procedures for the models that they will be installing or dismantling.

Advanced installers are trained as managers or supervisors. They will have the ability to plan, carry out a risk assessment and method statement, and to configure special arrangements, including special tie and anchor specifications.

For further information refer to:

- ☑ ***Lifting platforms – Mast climbing work platforms*** **(BS EN 1495)**
- ☑ ***Code of Practice for the installation, maintenance, thorough examination and safe use of mast climbing work platforms*** **(BS 7981)**
- ☑ **Chapter D02 Safe working at height.**

8.9 Telehandlers

Telehandlers (also known as rough terrain telescopic handlers or variable reach trucks) make a valuable contribution to the construction process by enabling materials to be unloaded from delivery vehicles, transported around construction sites and placed at height (reach). They are versatile machines that can be fitted with a wide range of attachments (such as buckets, skips, work platforms and crane jibs). The manufacturer's recommendations for the fitting and use of attachments should be followed. Unfortunately, there have been a significant number of accidents involving the use of telehandlers, which have tragically included a number of fatalities.

As with all lifting equipment the safe use of telehandlers requires selecting the right equipment, which has been adequately maintained, planning the operation effectively and having a trained and competent operator.

8.9.1 Types of telehandlers

Telehandlers fall into two broad categories, non-rotating and rotating.

8.9.1.1 Non-rotating

These machines comprise a powered wheeled chassis onto which is mounted a telescopic boom, pivoted on the chassis, which can be elevated from below the horizontal to an angle approaching the vertical. The outer end of the boom is fitted with a fork carriage and forks for handling unit loads. Levelling of the forks in the longitudinal plane, as the boom elevation changes, is carried out automatically.

Typical non-rotating telehandler

These machines are able to transport loads from one part of a site to another and place the load at height. On construction sites, the wheels are generally fitted with lug grip tyres to enable the chassis to negotiate unpaved ground. Various drive and steering configurations are available (such as two-wheeled drive, four-wheeled drive, pivot steer, rear-wheel steering and four-wheeled steering).

Many telehandlers are fitted with stabilisers that are deployed when the machine is stationary to provide additional stability and enhance the machine's lifting capacity. Telehandlers are often fitted with a feature that allows the chassis to be levelled laterally, where appropriate, before the boom is raised, when the machine is standing on uneven ground.

8.9.1.2 Rotating

Rotating telehandlers have all of the features of the non-rotating type, but with the addition of a rotating or slewing superstructure on which the boom and operator's cab are mounted. These machines also have outriggers fitted at either end of the chassis that enable the entire chassis to be lifted clear of the ground for maximum stability.

Typical rotating telehandler

The main advantages of these machines over the non-rotating type is compact chassis size, enhanced lifting height, increased stability and ease of placing loads without moving the chassis.

8.9.1.3 Telehandler attachments

Telehandlers are very versatile machines which, in addition to lifting of unit loads on forks, can be fitted with a wide range of attachments. Some examples are shown below.

- ☑ Sideshift forks.
- ☑ Sweepers.
- ☑ Block grabs.
- ☑ Tipping skips.
- ☑ Crane hooks.
- ☑ Crane jibs.
- ☑ Buckets (general purpose and material handling).
- ☑ Integrated access platforms.

It is essential that all attachments are compatible with the telehandler with which they are to be used. Where necessary and appropriate, the telehandler manufacturer should be consulted where third-party attachments are to be used. Planners and operators should be aware that attachments will alter the rated life capacity and centre of gravity of the machine.

8.9.1.4 Quick hitches

Some telehandlers are fitted with quick hitches or quick couplers, which enable attachments to be changed easily and rapidly. They fall into two types.

- **Mechanical quick hitch** where the hitch is engaged with the attachment, using the boom functions combined with fork carriage tilt. Once the quick hitch and attachment are engaged, a locking pin is inserted and secured with a retaining pin.
- **Hydraulic quick hitch** that is engaged in the same manner as the mechanical quick hitch but the locking pin is engaged hydraulically using the controls in the telehandler cab.

Both types of quick hitch can allow the attachment to become detached from the quick hitch if the manual locking pin is left out or the hydraulic locking pin fails to engage fully. There have been several serious injuries caused by falling attachments and misuse.

It is essential that operators get out of the cab to physically ensure that all quick hitches are securely locked before starting work with a newly attached attachment.

For further detailed guidance on quick hitches refer to the Strategic Forum for Construction's *Safe use of quick hitches on excavators* (Best practice guide).

8.9.2 Planning and use of telehandlers

The planning and carrying out of lifting operations with telehandlers should be in accordance with the principles set out in Chapter C07. In addition the points below should be taken into account.

8.9.2.1 Visibility

Restricted visibility when the boom is raised or when large loads are carried, as well as poor segregation, have been identified as a major cause of accidents involving pedestrians and telehandlers. Telehandlers are often fitted with aids to improve visibility and the operator's awareness of people in the vicinity of the telehandler. These aids should be in good working order and properly adjusted. It is the operator's responsibility to check the condition of all secondary aids to visibility and **not to use the machine** if they are not present or not working correctly. It is the supervisor's responsibility to fully support the operator in this action.

Some parts of a telehandler work cycle present particular challenges. A suspended load, for example, will clearly block some forward view, but the raised boom may also obscure the view to the side. If a telehandler is to lift suspended loads on site, the physical dimensions of the loads and their effect upon visibility must form part of the risk assessment.

If a telehandler is used to load or unload a truck, the partially raised boom will obstruct the view to the forward offside and may block the wing mirror that gives visibility to the rear offside. The safest way of using a telehandler to load/off-load is to keep the machine stationary and use the telescopic facility of the boom, rather than using the wheels. The driver of the truck should remain in a designated safe location for such operations.

Whilst the principal contractor has the primary responsibility to ensure adequate segregation and the supervisor must ensure that it is enforced, it remains the operator's responsibility to look around and check for the absence of pedestrians before moving and whilst manoeuvring and travelling. If the operator cannot see clearly, they should seek assistance or leave the cab to look around to confirm it is safe to continue the procedure.

8.9.2.2 Travelling on inclines, slopes and gradients

The telehandler must only operate on slopes or gradients at a speed designated by the site, taking into account ground conditions, to ensure that the operator has full control at all times.

Traffic routes should be on consolidated ground or may be temporary roadways giving equivalent safety. The slopes or gradients given in the table below are to assist planners in the preparation of traffic routes. They are the maximum gradients on which a telehandler can travel while being operated when crossing sites **in the standard travelling mode and at walking speed**. The standard travelling mode of a telehandler is with the boom retracted, the load/fork arms lowered to provide a clearance of 300 mm and not more than 500 mm (see manufacturer's instruction manual) from the ground to the upper faces of the fork arms, and the fork arms fully tilted rearwards.

Slope	%	Gradient	Angle
Maximum down slope	15%	1 in 6.66	8.5°
Maximum up slope			
Maximum lateral slope			

Operation on any traffic route with a greater slope or in a travelling mode different to the above should be subject to a site-specific risk assessment.

Consolidated ground is firm ground capable of accepting the mass of a loaded telehandler without significant deformation.

C 08

8.9.2.3 Stability of the telehandler

The stability of telehandlers and their loads are affected by the conditions of the ground on which they must stand when loading or unloading.

The area selected by the planners as a static loading area must be large enough to accommodate all the wheels of the telehandler and stabilisers or outriggers when fitted. The area should be of consolidated firm ground or surfaces giving similar levels of safety. It should be capable of accepting the mass of the loaded telehandler without significant deformation and be substantially level in both planes to ensure lateral and longitudinal stability when lifting operations are being carried out. Substantially level ground is defined as ground with a gradient of ideally 1% (1 in 100 gradient, 0.6°) but not more than the standard drainage slope of 2.5% (1 in 40 gradient, 1.4°).

When determining the area to be used for the unloading of lorries and the storage of materials, care should be taken to ensure the ground is consolidated and substantially level. The area provided must be large enough that the telehandler will not need to make tight turns with an elevated load.

A telehandler may be used for loading/unloading operations in areas that are not substantially level if they are used within their design capabilities. Where the achievement of a substantially level loading or unloading area is not reasonably practicable a risk assessment will be necessary.

Standard telehandlers are normally fitted with load movement indicators (LMI) and, in some cases, load movement limiters (LML). These prevent components (such as the boom) from extending if an overload situation is indicated. Due to their design the operator should never rely on the LMI as a way of checking whether the machine is safe to pick up a load. Refer to the lift plan and lift capacity charts of the machine at all times.

Load movement indicator units only warn of longitudinal instability and can become inaccurate and require resetting by a competent person on a regular basis.

Telehandlers become less stable in a lateral or sideways direction as the boom and load are raised and, because telehandlers normally have freely oscillating rear axles, the tipping lines form a triangle, rather than the rectangle of machines supported on outriggers (such as rotating boom telehandlers and mobile cranes). This has the effect of reducing lateral stability, particularly with the boom raised. These effects are shown in the diagrams below.

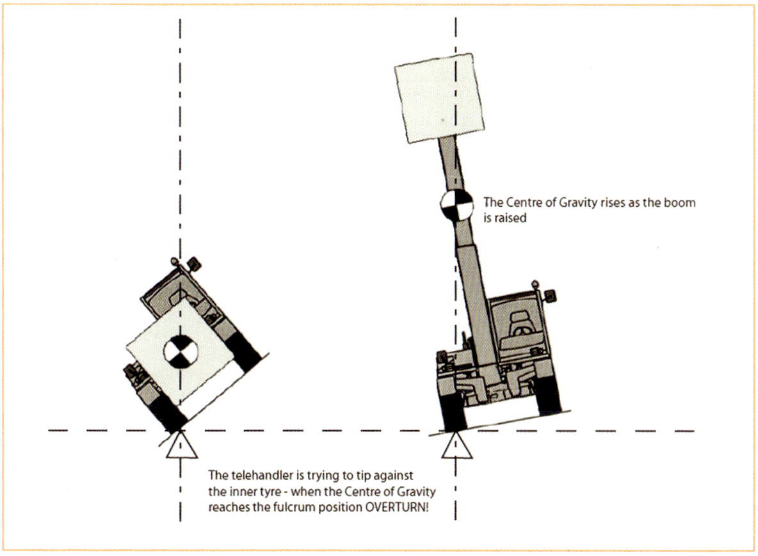

Lateral stability

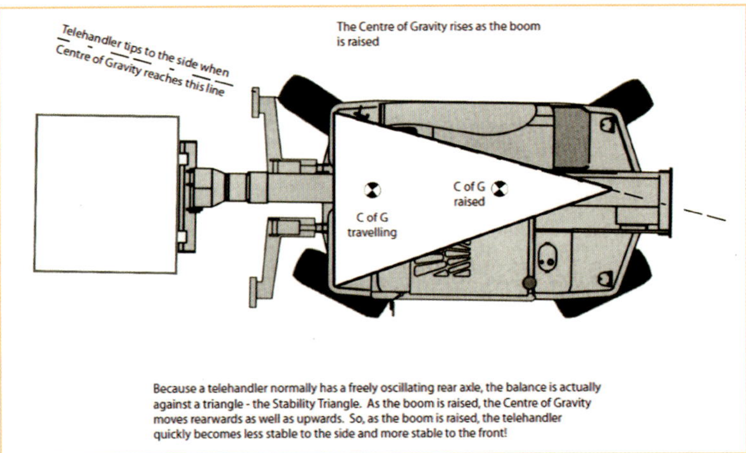

Typical stability triangle for non-rotating telehandle

When travelling with a load, the load should always be kept as near to the ground as possible.

Tyres play a vital part in the stability of telehandlers. Stability and load carrying capacity can be adversely affected by issues such as those shown below.

- Incorrect tyre pressures.
- Incorrect ply rating.
- Differences in diameter of tyres on the same axle due to differential wear.
- Use of tyres that are not of the required performance specification.
- Tyres with identical nominal sizes being of different physical size.
- Poor tyre repairs.

C 08

8.9.2.4 Wearing of seat belts

Telehandler cabs are provided with seat belts to restrain the operator and reduce the risk of serious injury in the event of a machine overturning. A survey of telehandler accidents in the UK carried out by the HSE shows that in seven years there have been at least 72 lateral overturns of telehandlers.

In three cases the operator was killed by being ejected from the cab and crushed; in a further two cases the operator was ejected from the cab and received serious crushing injuries. Had these operators been wearing their seat belts their deaths or injuries would probably have been avoided.

It is vital that operators of telehandlers wear the seat belt provided at all times – it could save their lives.

8.9.2.5 Stability of the load

When using a telehandler for loading or unloading a vehicle or stack, care must be taken to ensure that the load on the vehicle or stack is stable. Unless the correct sequence of loading or unloading is followed there is risk of the load becoming unstable with the potential for injury to persons in the vicinity.

Use of a wider fork carriage

- Loading should always be carried out with unloading in mind.
- Vehicles should always be loaded from the front or as directed by the vehicle driver, working from side to side and distributing the load evenly.
- Unloading should be carried out by reversing this sequence.
- When loading uncoupled articulated trailers, the first part of the load should be placed over the rear axle before loading from the front of the trailer.
- Care should also be taken to ensure that the part of the load on the vehicle or stack is not dislodged by contact with the telehandler carriage, forks or other attachments.
- During loading and unloading measures, such as exclusion zones or barriers, should be put in place to ensure that personnel are kept clear of falling loads.

- ☑ Before lifting a load it should be assessed to ensure that it will be stable and secure during lifting.
- ☑ The forks should always be evenly spaced on either side of the centre of gravity of the load.
- ☑ Long or irregularly shaped loads may have a centre of gravity that is close to the edges of the forks and may well result in the load falling during lifting.
- ☑ Long loads can be easier to control where a wider fork carriage is used and personnel should be kept clear of the load. They should **not** be asked to steady the load.

The practice of undercutting, where the load is lifted on the ends of the forks, rather than back at the heel, closest to the fork carriage, is often used when the load is to be placed adjacent to a wall or another item. This practice will reduce the rated capacity of the telehandler and may affect the stability of the load as its centre of gravity may be near or beyond the end of the forks.

8.9.2.6 Use of lifting hooks or crane jibs for suspended loads

Lifting and travelling with suspended loads is not the primary purpose of telehandlers. When selecting equipment for this activity the first step should be to ensure that a telehandler is suitable for carrying out the task safely. Where other equipment is more suitable, it should be used.

Using a telehandler to lift and travel with a suspended load is generally more hazardous than lifting unit loads on the forks of a telehandler. The operation should be effectively planned and communicated to all those involved. *(For further information refer to 7.4 Planning of lifting operations of Chapter C07).* The lifting of suspended loads should always be carried out with a telehandler that is fitted with a suitable lifting hook or attachment. If this can be shown to be not reasonably practicable, it is essential that any other method is justified by a robust risk assessment, taking account of the hierarchy of control.

Any lifting hook or crane jib should be marked with a rated capacity (safe working load) that must not be exceeded; the rated capacity of the hook may be less than the rated capacity of the telehandler or vice versa. It is important that the lower of the two values is used to determine the rated capacity of the combination. When working out the total weight of the load to be lifted, the weight of the lifting hook or crane jib and any lifting accessories (shackles, slings, and so on) must be taken into account.

Telehandler manufacturers supplying lifting hooks and crane jibs for their own machines will generally provide reduced rated capacities where suspended loads are being lifted and carried. This is intended to reduce the risk of overload or overturn due to displacement of the load through travelling, boom movements or the effect of wind.

Extreme care should be taken when travelling with a suspended load as any movement of the load will alter the load radius and may affect the stability of the telehandler. The position of the signaller should also be considered, as they are at risk from being in close proximity to a moving machine.

Basic telehandler operator training does not include lifting or travelling with suspended loads

If these tasks are to be carried out the employer must ensure that the operator is suitably trained and assessed as competent. The majority of basic training courses only deal with fork-mounted unit loads. Only training providers who can demonstrate having appropriate expertise of suspended loads and lifting operations with telehanders or mobile cranes should be selected. Any training should also include an appropriate element of slinging and signalling.

For further guidance on suspended loads refer to the Construction Plant Safety Group's *Lifting and travelling with suspended loads using telehandlers* (Good practice guide).

8.9.2.7 Use of telehandlers for the lifting of persons

Integrated work platform

Telehandlers are primarily intended for lifting materials and not people. However, they can be used with working platforms to allow people to work at height. It is generally accepted that, in conjunction with a telehandler, an integrated working platform provides a higher level of safety than a non-integrated type and should be used for the lifting of persons on construction sites, where a MEWP is not available.

C 08

Non-integrated platform attachments must not be used for planned tasks on construction sites.

8.9.3 Maintenance, checks and inspections of telehandlers

Telehandlers should be checked, maintained and inspected in accordance with 7.10 of Chapter C07. In addition the points below should be taken into account.

8.9.3.1 Tyre repair, replacement and maintenance

This section applies to pneumatic tyres only. Foam-filled tyres are not user serviceable.

Tyre pressure check

- Tyre pressures should be marked on the telehandler chassis adjacent to each wheel.
- Pressures should be checked daily when the tyres are cold.
- Tyre pressures should be the same for all tyres on the telehandler and should be within +5% and -0% of the manufacturer's specified pressure, unless a different tolerance is specified by the manufacturer.

  Note: *research undertaken by a major telehandler manufacturer indicates that -5% reduction in tyre pressure below the manufacturer's specified value can result in a 30% reduction in rated capacity at certain points on the load/height/radius curve.*
- Tyre pressure gauges should be of known accuracy (within +/- 1%).
- Where a tyre is found to be significantly under pressure no attempt should be made to re-inflate it and return the machine to use. It is essential that the cause is investigated by a competent tyre specialist, as this may well be an indication of imminent tyre failure.

Tyre inflation applies to tyres fitted on single piece wheels. Where multi-piece wheels are fitted or there is any doubt about the type of wheel, a competent tyre specialist should be consulted.

For tyres fitted on multi-piece wheels refer to the BITA publication *Multi-piece pneumatic tyred wheels – Inspection, maintenance and repairs* (GN67).

- Air should be added, if required, inflating to the pressure specified in the manufacturer's manual.
- Before starting inflation a personnel exclusion zone of at least 3 m around the machine should be established by the use of barriers, cones, and so on *(refer to image below)*.
- Personnel inflating tyres should stand a minimum of 3 m away from the tyre and outside the likely explosion trajectory to avoid injury in the event of a failure. This will require at least 3 m of airline between the nozzle and the airline trigger mechanism *(refer to image below)*.
- Personnel should ensure that they stand on the other side of the telehandler when inflating *(refer to image below)*.
- Tyre valves should be checked to ensure that they are not leaking. Valve stem caps should always be replaced.

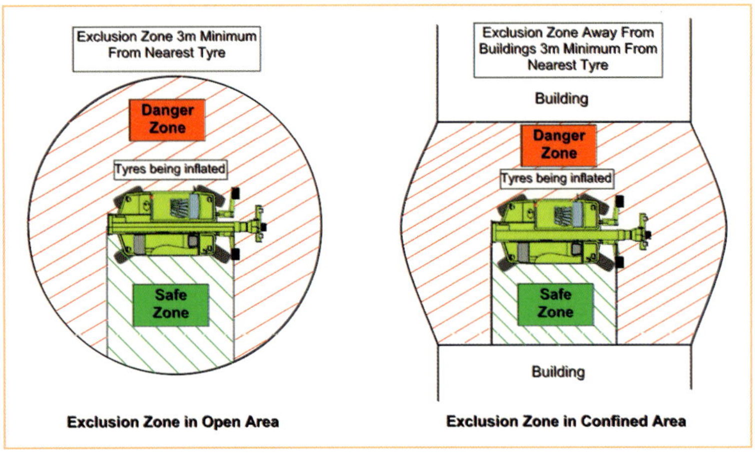

Tyre inflation safe zones and exclusion zones

For further detailed guidance on the safe inflation of tyres refer to the HSE publication *Safety during tyre inflation in motor vehicle repair* (INDG433).

A real life example of tyre issues

A telehandler operator had been checking the tyre pressures on his machine. Having completed the checks, he was walking away from the machine and one of the tyres exploded. Subsequent investigation revealed that the tyre, which had recently been replaced, was 14 ply with a 3.5 tonne load rating rather than the manufacturer's specification of 16 ply with a 6 tonne rating.

The contractor also found that the tyre had been ordered from their approved supplier by asking for a tyre for that model of telehandler, without any mention of ply or load rating. A subsequent check of other machines found that 30% were fitted with incorrect tyres.

Tyre damage. All tyres should be inspected daily. The tread and side walls should be checked for bulges, separation and cuts.

For pneumatic tyres, when any cut, rip or tear is discovered that exposes sidewall or tread area cords in the tyre, measures must be taken to remove the product from service immediately. Arrangements must be made for replacement of the tyre or tyre assembly.

Tyre replacement. Telehandler manufacturers generally list a range of approved tyres in the parts manual for a specific machine. If not using an approved replacement tyre then consult with a competent tyre specialist and ensure the replacement tyres have the following characteristics.

- ✓ Same physical size as the original.
- ✓ Equal or greater ply and load rating as the original.
- ✓ Tyre tread contact width equal or greater than original.
- ✓ Equivalent performance specification.

Unless specifically approved by the telehandler manufacturer, foam-filled or ballast-filled tyre assemblies must not be replaced with pneumatic tyres.

When a tyre is being replaced it is essential that the condition of the other tyres on the machine is assessed by a competent tyre specialist and appropriate action taken. This may include moving part worn tyres around, to ensure that the telehandler is substantially level when standing on a flat, level surface.

If tyres on opposite sides are different sizes the telehandler boom will not be vertical when the machine is standing on level ground. This will cause the combined centre of gravity of the telehandler and load to move sideways, which may lead to instability.

8.9.3.2 Wheel replacement

It is essential that replacement wheels have the same diameter, width and offset dimensions as the originals.

8.9.4 Thorough examination of telehandlers

The thorough examination of telehandlers should be carried out in accordance with 7.11 of Chapter C07.

For further information on the safe use of telehandlers refer to the Strategic Forum for Construction Plant Safety Group's *Safe use of telehandlers in construction* (Good practice guide).

8.10 Excavators used as cranes

The use of excavators for lifting operations, particularly on construction sites, has become more common over the last few years. Excavators and backhoes are designed for rapid earth moving and are not designed for lifting operations as their principal function. When planning a lifting operation, consideration should be given as to whether an excavator is the most appropriate machine, taking into account the type of lift and the duration of the task.

The use of an excavator or backhoe for lifting creates additional hazards for personnel in the vicinity. Under normal circumstances, personnel are kept away from the working area around the bucket of an excavator, as this is considered to be a hazardous area. Where the excavator is used for object handling, however, the slinger has to be in the danger area in order to hook the load onto the hooking device. This puts the slinger at risk of being struck by the load, bucket or excavator arm if the excavator moves without warning.

8.10.1 Planning and use of excavators used as cranes

The planning and carrying out of lifting operations with excavators should be in accordance with the principles set out in Chapter C07. In addition the points below should be taken into account.

8.10.1.1 Excavator requirements when used for lifting

The design of earthmoving machinery for lifting (object handling) is covered by the European standard BS EN 474 Parts 1, 3, 4 and 5.

Any earthmoving machine designed for object handling should have a rated object-handling capacity table available inside the cab. If a rated object-handling capacity table is not available then the machine should not be used for object handling.

Handling attachments (for example, grab) that do not require the assistance of a person for hooking or guiding are considered to be part of normal earthmoving operations and do not require warning devices and a rated capacity table.

An earthmoving machine used for lifting operations must be fitted with a load hooking device. If the load hooking device is a hook then this should have a clip or other device that prevents a sling slipping off the hook. Many quick hitches provide a load hooking device in the design of the hitch.

If the rated lifting capacity for an excavator or the backhoe portion of a backhoe/loader is greater than one tonne (or the overturning moment is greater than 40,000 Nm) then the machine must be fitted with the following.

- A boom-lowering control device on the raising boom cylinder(s) that meets the requirements of ISO 8643:1997.
- An acoustic or visual warning device that indicates to the operator when the object-handling capacity or corresponding load moment is reached.

A change in the definition of rated object handling capacity in the latest version of EN 474 has affected new excavators manufactured and CE marked after 29 December 2009. It requires any new excavator that has a rated capacity of over one tonne, and which is going to be used for lifting, to be fitted with an RCI and check valves.

Previously some manufacturers had been marking the excavator for a rated **lifting capacity** of one tonne even though it had a **rated capacity** in excess of this. Excavators manufactured and CE marked before 29 December 2009 are not affected by these changes.

Loaders and the loader portion of a backhoe/loader do not require a boom lowering control device or acoustic/visual warning devices.

Where a risk assessment shows that there is a significant risk of overloading and/or overturning on machines with a rated capacity of one tonne or less, a rated capacity indicator may be required. (*Refer to LOLER ACoP and Guidance paragraph 122.*)

C
08

Suitable slings must be available to attach the load to the excavator. Slings and other lifting accessories should be CE marked, and marked with the rated capacity (SWL).

Whilst BS 7121 may not specifically refer to excavators used as cranes, compliance with all the appropriate parts of BS 7121 would assist in the provision of safe systems of work as required by Section 2(2) of the Health and Safety at Work Act 1974.

8.10.1.2 Quick hitches

The quick hitches fitted to excavators and other earthmoving plant make a valuable contribution to the construction process by enabling buckets and other attachments to be attached and detached rapidly, as required. Unfortunately, there have been a significant number of accidents involving the use of quick hitches, which have included a number of fatalities.

When using quick hitches the following precautions should be observed. These precautions are applicable to all types of quick hitch (manual, semi-automatic and all fully automatic types), including those that lock onto both pins. All types of quick hitch can be safely used by competent people within a safe system of work. This will involve planning, training, instruction, communication, supervision and maintenance. However, all types of quick hitch may fail if they are not used and maintained correctly.

- Keep other workers away from the machine's working range. Never work under the bucket or attachment and ensure that the operator isolates the controls if there are other workers in the machine's working range. Ensure that your site supervisors enforce this rule.
- Make sure that your operators are aware of their personal and legal responsibility to use all quick hitches safely. Serious misuse of quick hitches should always be treated as gross misconduct, which could lead to dismissal or prosecution.
- Check that all operators confirm that the quick hitch is in place every time they change an attachment. It is essential that this is done by close inspection at the quick hitch, which will normally entail the operator getting down from the cab. It is good practice to make this a requirement for all quick hitches.
- Check that site supervisors understand that the operator has to fully confirm that the quick hitch is in place. Make sure site supervisors allow operators time to do this.
- Check that site supervisors monitor that operators are confirming proper engagement, by spot checks.
- Check that machines are in good order, and all quick hitches are included in the maintenance plan and subject to proper maintenance.
- Check that operators and maintenance personnel have specific instructions for the combination of machine, quick hitch and attachment.
- Confirm that operators are competent to use the specific quick hitch in accordance with the manufacturer's instructions and your safe system of work.
- Forbid practices such as pick and place (moving attachments without properly engaging the locking devices).

8.10.1.3 Using quick hitches with other attachments

Contractors may want to use quick hitches with attachments other than a bucket in normal configuration. However, if a specific application, such as the fitting of vibratory hammers or reversing of buckets, is not explicitly allowed by the manufacturer, the user should assume that it is not allowed, and should not use the quick hitch for this attachment or application. Quick hitches should only be used with attachments and in applications as specified by the manufacturer.

It is essential that operators get out of the cab to physically ensure that all quick hitches are securely locked before starting work with a new attachment.

For further detailed guidance on quick hitches refer to the Strategic Forum for Construction's *Safe use of quick hitches on excavators* (Best practice guide).

8.10.1.4 Lifting of persons with excavators

Excavators should not be used under any circumstances for the lifting of persons as they are primarily designed for excavating with a bucket and consequently are capable of operating speeds and movements that make them totally unsuitable for the lifting of persons.

8.10.1.5 Load attachment

Where the hooking device (the point on the machine designed for connection of the load) is not part of the bucket, the bucket should (where possible, and unless the manufacturer's instructions specify otherwise) be removed in order to improve visibility and reduce the weight being lifted. If the bucket is retained, then the weight of both the bucket and quick hitch has to be added to the load when determining whether the load is within the rated capacity.

When attaching lifting slings to the hooking device or lifting point care should be taken to ensure that the slings and their attachments are able to hang free at all times.

Attachment using a shackle may limit rotation if, for example, a pipe suspended from the slings is to be turned end to end

Using a swivel to overcome this problem

If the quick hitch is tilted backwards and/or the dipper arm is raised, the master link of the sling and any attachments may bend or twist – possibly leading to damage or failure.

Hitch tilted backwards with master link subject to bending

Hitch tilted backwards with master link subject to twisting

Good practice of chain and master link hanging freely without obstruction

For further guidance on planning and carrying out lifting operations with excavators refer to the Construction Plant-hire Association's *Guidance on lifting operations in construction when using excavators*.

8.10.2 Maintenance, checks and inspections of excavators used as cranes

Excavators should be checked, maintained and inspected in accordance with 7.10 of Chapter C07.

8.10.3 Thorough examination of excavators used as cranes

The thorough examination of excavators used as cranes should be carried out in accordance with 7.11 of Chapter C07. In addition the following points should be taken into account.

8.10.3.1 Thorough examination of quick hitches

Quick hitches used for lifting fall under the thorough examination requirements of the Lifting Operations and Lifting Equipment Regulations (LOLER), whilst those not used for lifting fall under the inspection requirements of the Provision and Use of Work Equipment Regulations (PUWER).

The periodic examination and/or inspection of quick hitches forms a vital addition to planned preventive maintenance. It provides evidence of the adequacy of a maintenance regime and highlights any deficiencies, leading to improved reliability and safety of the hitch being used.

The requirements for examination and/or inspection vary with the type of hitch. Consequently the type of examination/inspection and the frequency at which it occurs is a decision for the competent person carrying out the examination/inspection.

For information on the legal minimum requirements for quick hitches see the current version of the HSE *Sector information minute* 02/2007/01. In all cases, seek guidance from the competent person regarding the most appropriate regime for a particular hitch.

Quick hitches

The nature and extent of both LOLER thorough examinations and PUWER inspections are risk based and since the risks associated with quick hitch failure are similar for lifting and non-lifting duties, good practice requires that all quick hitches:

- that remain permanently fitted to a machine, are thoroughly examined and/or inspected at the same time as the base machine
- suitable for lifting (fitted with a lifting eye), which are regularly removed from the machine (as interchangeable equipment), are subjected to a periodic thorough examination at intervals not exceeding six months.

All quick hitches subject to thorough examination must be permanently marked with a unique identification number. If a quick hitch does not have such a number, the owner/user must ensure that one is applied.

Reports of thorough examination should contain the details required by Schedule 1 of LOLER.

Refer to Appendix D of Chapter C07 Lifting operations.

Thorough examinations should be carried out by competent persons who have the genuine authority and independence to ensure that examinations are properly carried out and that the necessary recommendations arising from them are made impartially.

8.10.3.2 Thorough examination/inspection following major alteration, damage or incident

If the quick hitch has been subjected to major alteration, repair, damage or has been involved in an incident, it should be thoroughly examined/inspected before it is put back into service.

e.g. Major alterations

- Alteration of attachment mechanisms.
- Attachment of lifting eyes.
- Modification of pin bores.
- Application of heat.

8.11 Lifting accessories

Ropes, chains, eye bolts and slings are all examples of lifting accessories. They must be clearly marked with their safe working load.

All lifting accessories must also be:

- properly constructed and maintained
- free of any defect or damage likely to affect their strength
- regularly maintained and inspected
- thoroughly examined
- securely attached to the lifting equipment (for example, the crane) and the load
- used within their safe working load.

Accessories used for lifting must be inspected and thoroughly examined at a maximum of six monthly intervals, with records kept as specified in Chapter C07.

8.11.1 Marking

All lifting accessories must be clearly marked with their rated capacity (SWL) and carry an identifying mark. Where this is not possible then a coding system (such as a tag or colour code) should be used to allow the user to determine the safe working load. A lifting accessory may also be marked with its own weight, which is a consideration when assessing the total load to be lifted.

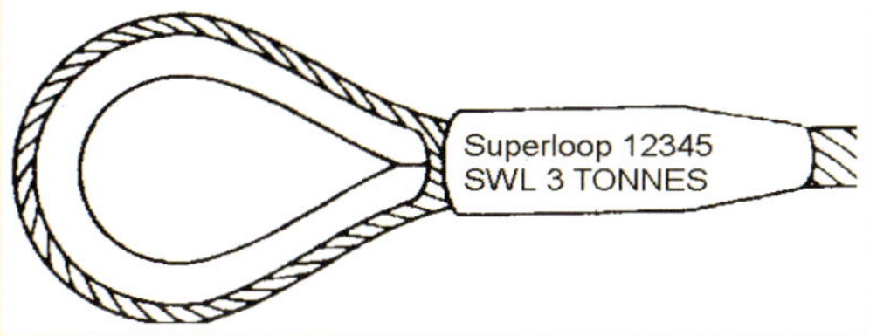

Where the rated capacity (SWL) depends on the configuration of a lifting accessory (such as a two leg chain) then the rated capacity (SWL) for each configuration should be clearly marked on the equipment using a tag or by a chart available at the point of use.

8.11.2 Overloading

Lifting accessories must never be overloaded except under test conditions authorised by an experienced and competent person.

8.11.3 Preventing damage

The edges and corners of a load should be packed to prevent sharp edges damaging lifting ropes, chains or slings.

8.11.4 Hooks

All hooks used for lifting must be fitted with a safety catch, or should be moused, or otherwise shaped to prevent the sling eye or load coming off the hook.

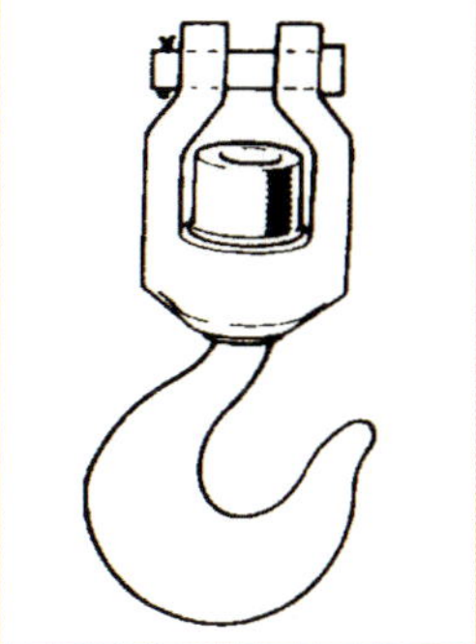

Open top swivel hook

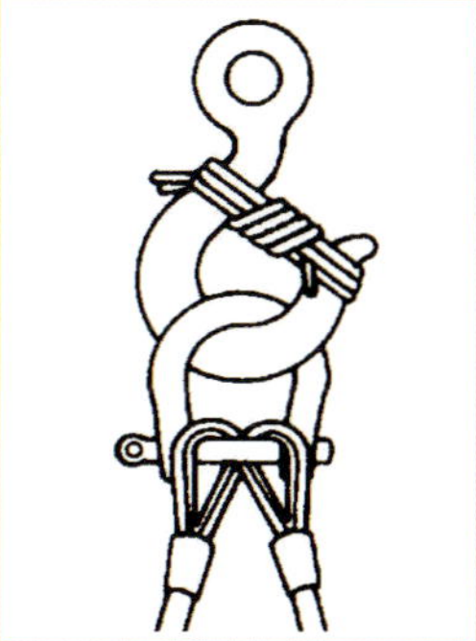

Moused hook

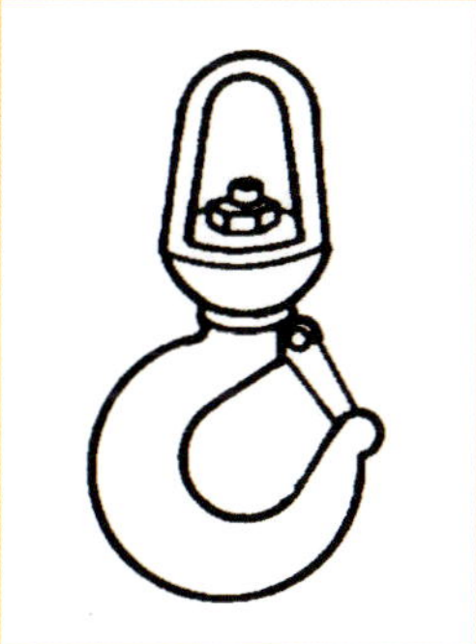

Hook with spring

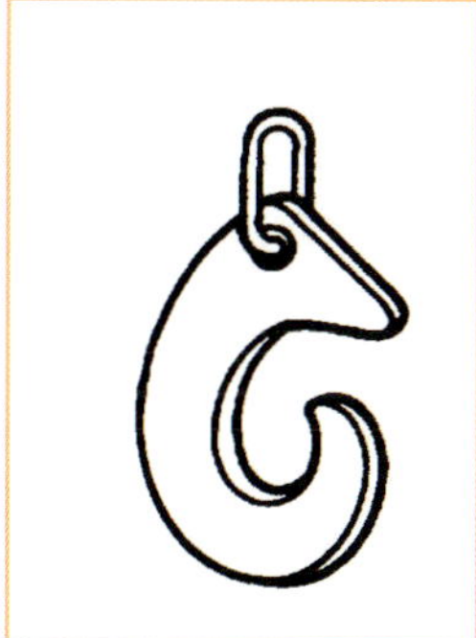

'C' hook with link-loaded safety catch

8.11.5 Slings

Slings must be attached correctly to the lifting equipment by an approved method, either by securing the ring directly onto the hook if size permits, or by use of a suitable shackle, fitted with the pin of the shackle on the hook and the load suspended from the bow.

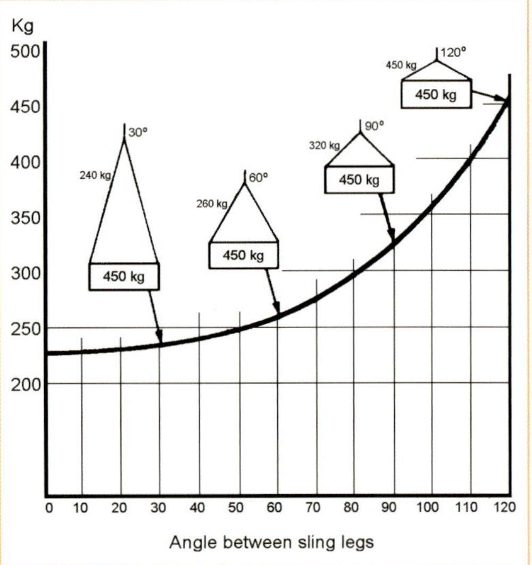

Good practice showing the load in each sling leg increasing as the angle between the sling legs is increased

The correct method of slinging will vary with the types of load, the different materials or items lifted. It is essential to see that the load is secure. Care must be taken to see that slings are not damaged, and suspect or defective slings must be discarded.

Dog ropes or tag lines, securely attached to the end of the load, should be used when handling long or large loads, to direct the load into position and prevent it spinning. Tag lines should be as short as possible.

Multiple slings (two-legged, three-legged, and so on) must be connected by a ring or shackle and the load properly distributed so that no leg is overloaded. Chandelier lifting (using each leg to lift a load at different heights) must not be undertaken when using multi-legged slings as this would place the slinger in danger when detaching the load.

When in use, the angles between sling legs should be less than 90°. At angles greater than this, the strain on each leg increases very rapidly to a point where they may break because of overloading.

With a simple two-legged parallel sling, the load on each leg is half the total load. As the angle between sling legs increases, the load on each sling leg increases to approximately double at an angle of 120°.

With a sling angle of 90°, the rated capacity (SWL) of the sling should be at least 43% greater than the nominal weight of the load.

8.11.6 Repaired lifting accessories

Any lifting accessory (chain, sling, and so on) that has been altered or repaired by welding must be thoroughly examined and tested before taking it back into use. The record of thorough examination should be kept until at least the next scheduled thorough examination.

Knotted ropes, chains or slings and those that have been shortened or joined by nuts and bolts through the links must not be used.

Any lifting accessory that is thought to have suffered a loss of strength, been damaged or overloaded, or is otherwise defective, should be withdrawn from use and quarantined. The equipment should be scrapped or re-examined by a competent person who will recommend that either it can be put back into service or must be disposed of.

8.11.7 Construction of slings

Slings are available in a wide range of styles made from many different materials to suit particular purposes.

Chain slings are made from various grades of steel. They can stretch and the links, rings or hooks may become distorted and fracture if subject to excess stress.

Chain slings should only be shortened by using the correct shortening clutches. Chains must not be knotted or joined by nuts and bolts. Hooks must be of the 'C' type or fitted with a safety latch.

Wire rope slings are made from drawn steel wire. Each leg of the sling will have an eye formed at either end. Wire rope slings may be damaged when kinked sharply or if put under stress when twisted. Steel wire rope may be damaged by corrosion through poor care and storage.

Wire rope slings must not be made up on site using bulldog grips.

Wire ropes and slings are of many different types of construction, each having properties related to usage. It is therefore important, when ordering an item, to specify the intended use.

Fibre rope slings might be made from natural fibres (manila, sisal, hemp) or synthetic fibres. Slings made from natural fibres can be prone to rotting. Only purpose-made slings, clearly marked with their rated capacity (SWL), should be used on site.

On no account should slings be fabricated from lengths of rope found lying around the site. Fibre rope slings are more easily cut or damaged, and should be visually examined by a competent person every time before use to ensure they are serviceable. Natural fibre ropes should not be used for making up slings on site.

Synthetic fibre ropes do not rot but can be affected by some chemicals. Care should be taken to avoid contamination with alkalis or acids. **Suspect or contaminated synthetic fibre ropes and slings must not be used.**

Flat lifting slings are used where special lifting operations are required and afford a certain amount of protection to the load.

Flat and round slings may be made of woven synthetic materials (such as nylon, polyester, polypropylene and Terylene) with 'eyes' sewn in, or plastic-coated wire mesh, or formed by a series of plaited wire ropes between two end fittings. These might also be covered with a plastic material. All woven materials are prone to damage and should be regularly checked for serviceability. Slings should be protected from sharp edges and placed evenly about the load, not twisted. Care must be taken to see that the rated capacity (SWL) is not reduced by having a sling angle greater than 90°.

8.11.8 Shackles

Two types of shackle are commonly used in lifting operations. They are the **bow type** shackle and **dee type** shackle, both of which are available with threaded or plain pins.

Only bow type shackles may be used to suspend a load from a hook. The shackle must be positioned with the pin across the hook and the load suspended from the bow. If necessary, spacers should be fitted over the pin to centralise the shackle on the hook.

Overloading, out-of-balance loads and misuse can distort shackles; they should be checked regularly for shape and wear.

8.11.9 Eyebolts

Eyebolts are made to screw into or through a load and may be plain (dynamo) or have collars, with or without links. The plain eyebolt is good only for vertical loading. Even when a collared eyebolt is used, the safe working load is reduced if the load to which it is attached initially lifted at an angle.

Collared eyebolts with links may be used providing the angle of load to the axis of eyebolt thread does not exceed 15°. Over 15°, safe working loads must be derated in accordance with BS EN ISO 3266 *Forged steel eyebolts Grade 4* for general lifting purposes.

When installed, the collar must be at right angles to the hole, should be in full contact with the surface, and be properly tightened.

The load should always be applied in the plane of the eye, never in the other direction. If necessary, washers or shims should be inserted below the collar to ensure that the eye is correctly aligned when tight.

Extreme care must be taken to ensure that metric threaded eyebolts are not inserted in imperial threaded holes. Although these might appear to match, it is an interference fit only, and the mechanical strength may be almost nothing.

8.11.10 Bulldog grips (wire rope grips)

Bulldog grips, if used properly to make an eye with a thimble, provide a simple and effective means of securing the ends of wire ropes instead of splicing or socketing. The final rated capacity (SWL) will be about 75% of that of the wire. It is essential that the correct size and type of grip is used, that the wire is clean and that the correct torque is applied when tightening the grips.

Bulldog grips must be fitted with the 'U' bolt on the dead or tail end of the line (non-load-bearing end). There must be no deviation from this practice.

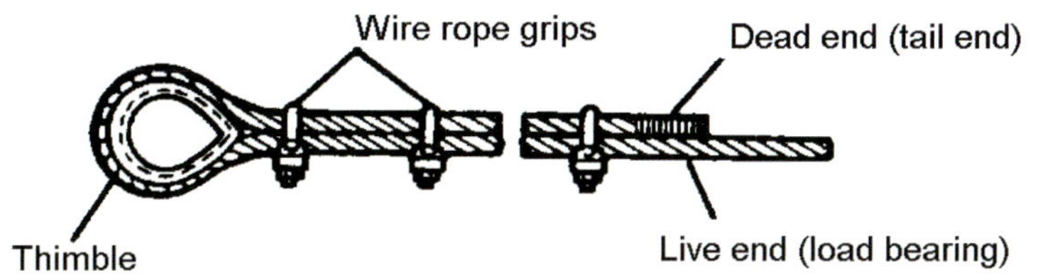

Correct method of fitting wire rope grips

The number of wire rope grips shown in the above illustration is insufficient. The figure is schematic only.

Wire rope grips meeting the requirements of BS EN 13411 are efficient when correctly installed by a competent person. Generally, when using wire rope grips, the previous numbers of grips should be used and they should be tightened to the relevant torque. However, in all cases, the manufacturer's recommendations, in addition to the advice given in the standard, should be closely followed.

Maximum nominal rope diameter (mm)	Required number of wire rope grips	Tightening torque required (Nm)
5	3	2.0
6.5	3	3.5
8	4	6.0
10	4	9.0
12	4	20.0
14	4	33.0
16	4	49.0
19	4	68.0
22	5	107.0
26	5	147.0
30	6	212.0
34	6	296.0
40	6	363.0

The wire should be in good condition and all threads and nuts should be suitably greased.

The first bulldog grip should be fitted as close as possible to the thimble and, thereafter, at a spacing of no greater than six times the rope diameter.

Nuts must be tightened to the relevant torque:

- when the rope is assembled
- when taken into use
- on the application of the load
- at periodic intervals when in continuous use.

If the above criteria are not followed, then the strength of the eye and thimble will be considerably reduced. If the criteria are neglected for an extended period, the eye and thimble may fail.

Wire rope grips must not be used to make lifting slings, long splices, or to join two wire ropes, other than with thimbles or eyes.

For intermediate diameters of rope, the next larger size wire rope grip should be used, except as follows.

- The size 5 mm grip should only be used on a nominal 5 mm diameter rope.
- For 11 mm diameter rope, use four 10 mm rope grips tightened to a torque of 14 Nm.

8.11.11 Maintenance, checks and inspections of lifting accessories

Lifting accessories should be checked, maintained and inspected in accordance with 7.10 of Chapter C07.

8.11.12 Thorough examination of lifting accessories

The thorough examination of lifting accessories should be carried out in accordance with 7.11 of Chapter C07.

For further guidance on the selection, use, maintenance, inspection and thorough examination of lifting accessories, and planning and carrying out lifting operations with excavators, refer to the Lifting Equipment Engineers' Association *Code of Practice for the safe use of lifting equipment.*

Appendix A – MEWP reception and inspection report guidance

These guidance notes are provided to assist the persons appointed by the site manager to complete reports.

The term MEWP covers pedestrian-controlled, self-propelled and power-operated mobile elevating work and access platforms. The types of plant typically covered by the MEWP reception report are as follows.

- ☑ Scissor lifts.
- ☑ Telescopic boom or jibs.
- ☑ Articulating and telescopic booms.
- ☑ Towable units.
- ☑ Vehicle mounted.
- ☑ Self-propelled, or pedestrian controlled.

In the case of plant provided by a plant hirer, at the site manager's discretion, a competent person appointed by the plant hirer may conduct the inspection and complete the report. In all other cases the inspection must be carried out by the contractor's appointed person.

In the case of plant owned or hired by a contractor, then a competent person employed by the contractor may conduct the inspection and complete the report.

All completed MEWP reception reports shall be retained for inspection on site.

The report is produced in a checklist format for ease of use and is intended to provide a means by which the condition of all plant delivered to site can be checked by the appointed person. All questions shall record an answer, with a suitable comment or action included when necessary.

The appointed person is also required to confirm the validity of relevant statutory documentation (such as test certificates) and thorough examination and inspection reports.

An aide memoir is provided below to assist the appointed person on statutory requirements that apply to certain items of plant.

MEWP	Regime	Comments	Documentation
All types of mobile elevating work platform (MEWPS).	Thorough examination: ■ current six monthly (LOLER) ■ after 1,000 operational hours or as stated in the manufacturer's guidance, if different ■ after major repair or modification ■ following an incident. **Note:** *conducted by a competent engineering surveyor/fitter with reports kept for two years.*	■ Fitted with suitable devices to prevent persons being crushed, trapped, struck or falling when riding or working from carrier. ■ Provision of suitable devices to prevent risk of a carrier failing. ■ Safe means of escape for persons trapped in a carrier.	Evidence of six-monthly thorough examination, including certification of a SWL.
	Weekly maintenance inspection conducted by a competent operator or fitter.		Evidence of weekly inspection.
	Daily (pre-use) visual inspection conducted by a competent operator.		Evidence of daily inspection.

Following completion of the report at receipt of the MEWP on site, formal inspection/examination must be recorded weekly in normal operating conditions, or under higher risk conditions, daily.

For a MEWP reception and inspection report form refer to Section G: *Checklists and forms.*

C 08

Index